KT-234-573
510

REVISE S2

for MEI Structured Mathematics

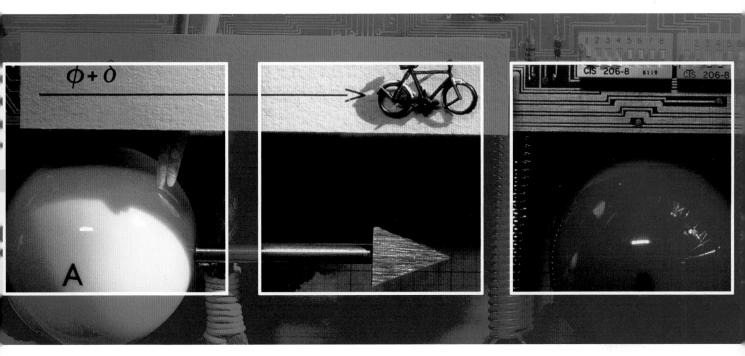

Series Editor
Roger Porkess

Author
Stella Dudzic

HODDER
EDUCATION
AN HACHETTE UK COMPANY

Every effort has been made to trace all copyright holders, but if any have been inadvertently overlooked the Publishers will be pleased to make the necessary arrangements at the first opportunity.

Although every effort has been made to ensure that website addresses are correct at time of going to press, Hodder Education cannot be held responsible for the content of any website mentioned in this book. It is sometimes possible to find a relocated web page by typing in the address of the home page for a website in the URL window of your browser.

Hachette UK's policy is to use papers that are natural, renewable and recyclable products and made from wood grown in sustainable forests. The logging and manufacturing processes are expected to conform to the environmental regulations of the country of origin.

Orders: please contact Bookpoint Ltd, 130 Milton Park, Abingdon, Oxon OX14 4SB.
Telephone: (44) 01235 827720. Fax: (44) 01235 400454. Lines are open 9.00 – 5.00, Monday to Saturday, with a 24-hour message answering service.
Visit our website at www.hoddereducation.co.uk

© Stella Dudzic, Roger Porkess, 2010
First published in 2010 by
Hodder Education,
An Hachette UK Company
338 Euston Road
London NW1 3BH

Impression number   5 4 3 2 1
Year   2013 2012 2011 2010

Dynamic Learning Student Online website © Stella Dudzic, Roger Porkess, 2010; with contributions from Elise Heighway and Louisa Mousley; developed by Infuze Limited and MMT Limited; cast: Tom Frankland; recorded at Alchemy Soho.

All rights reserved. Apart from any use permitted under UK copyright law, no part of this publication may be reproduced or transmitted in any form or by any means, electronic or mechanical, including photocopying and recording, or held within any information storage and retrieval system, without permission in writing from the publisher or under licence from the Copyright Licensing Agency Limited. Further details of such licences (for reprographic reproduction) may be obtained from the Copyright Licensing Agency Limited, Saffron House, 6–10 Kirby Street, London EC1N 8TS.

Typeset in 11/12 Helvetica by Tech-Set Ltd., Gateshead, Tyne & Wear
Printed in India

A catalogue record for this title is available from the British Library

ISBN: 978 0 340 957448

Contents

Introduction

Welcome to this Revision Guide for the MEI Statistics 2 unit!

The book is organised into 20 sections covering the various topics in the syllabus. A typical section is four pages long; the first three pages contain essential information and key worked examples covering the topic. At the start of each chapter, there are page references to where the section topics are covered in the textbook.

The last page in each section has questions for you to answer so that you can be sure that you have really understood the topic. There is a multiple-choice exercise and an exam-style question. If you are to gain the greatest possible benefit from the book, and so do your best in the Statistics 2 exam, you should work through these for yourself and then refer to the accompanying website to check your answers.

The multiple-choice questions cover the basic ideas and techniques. It is really important that you work through them carefully; guessing will do you no good at all. When you have decided on the answer you think is right, enter it on the website. If you are right, it tells you so and gives the full solution; check that your answer wasn't just a fluke. If your choice is not right, the website gives you advice about your mistake; the possible wrong answers have all been designed to pick out particular common misunderstandings. The explanations on the website are based on the most likely mistakes; even if you make a different mistake, you will usually find enough help to set you on the right path so that you can try again.

When you come onto the exam-style question, write out your best possible answer. Then go to the website. You will find the solution displayed step-by-step, together with someone talking you through it and giving you helpful advice.

So the book contains the essential information to revise for the exam and, critically, also enables you to check that you have understood it properly. That is a recipe for success.

Finally, a word of warning. This book is designed to be used together with the textbook and not as a replacement for it. This Revision Guide will help you to prepare for the exam but to do really well you also need the deep understanding that comes from the detailed explanations you will find in the textbook.

Good learning and good luck!

Stella Dudzic, Roger Porkess

Where you see the following icon **DL**, please refer to the Dynamic Learning Student Online website. Information on how to access this website is printed on the inside front cover of the book.

Accompanying books
MEI Structured Mathematics S2
ISBN 978 0 340 88853 7

Companion to Advanced Mathematics and Statistics
ISBN 978 0 340 95923 7

The Poisson distribution

Poisson probabilities using the formula

A | ABOUT THIS TOPIC

The Poisson distribution can be thought of as the probability distribution of the number of occurrences of a 'rare event'. It can be used for modelling the number of atoms which undergo radioactive decay per minute, the number of misprints per page in a book, the number of goals scored in a football game and many other events.

R | REMEMBER

- Discrete random variables from S1:
  - The expectation of the random variable, X, is denoted by $E(X)$. It is sometimes called 'the expected value'.
  - The variance of X is denoted by $Var(X)$; the symbol σ^2 is often used to stand for the variance, with σ for the standard deviation.
- Factorials from S1:
  - $n! = n(n - 1)(n - 2)... \times 3 \times 2 \times 1$.
- Probability rules from S1:
  - If A and B are independent events then $P(A \cap B) = P(A)P(B)$, where $A \cap B$ is the *intersection of events* (A and B); (they both occur).
  - For mutually exclusive events, $P(A \cup B) = P(A) + P(B)$, where $A \cup B$ is the *union of events* (A or B); (one or both of them occurs).

K | KEY FACTS

- A discrete random variable may be modelled by a Poisson distribution if:
  - events occur at random and independently of each other
  - the average number of events in a given interval of time or space is a constant, λ.
- If X is the number of occurrences in a given interval then
  $$P(X = r) = e^{-\lambda} \frac{\lambda^r}{r!} \text{ for } r = 0, 1, 2, 3, 4, ...$$
- There is no limit to the possible number of occurrences in a given interval but the probabilities for large values of r get very small.
- $E(X) = Var(X) = \lambda$.

What is the Poisson distribution?

The Poisson distribution can be used to work out probabilities for a variety of naturally occurring processes. It has applications in science and business and is named after the French mathematician Simeon Poisson.
- A discrete random variable may be modelled by a Poisson distribution if:
  - events occur at random and independently of each other
  - the average number of events in a given interval of time or space is a constant, λ.

A | ADVICE

It is important to know when it is appropriate to use the Poisson distribution. In exam questions you will be told that you should be using a Poisson distribution but often you will have to explain why such a distribution is appropriate.

EXAMPLE 1

A local health authority is monitoring the number of people in its area who suffer from a particular disease. The disease is highly contagious. Over the past year, they found that, on average, 2.6 people per week had the disease. Explain why the Poisson distribution may not be appropriate for this situation.

SOLUTION

The Poisson distribution can be used if events occur independently of each other. The disease is contagious so occurrences are unlikely to be independent.

r	P(X = r)
0	0.074 273 578 214
1	0.193 111 303 357
2	0.251 044 694 364
3	0.217 572 068 449
4	0.141 421 844 492
5	0.073 539 359 136
6	0.031 867 055 626
7	0.011 836 334 947
8	0.003 846 808 858
9	0.001 111 300 337
10	0.000 288 938 088
11	0.000 068 294 457
12	0.000 014 797 132
13	0.000 002 959 426
14	0.000 000 549 608
15	0.000 000 095 265
16	0.000 000 015 481
17	0.000 000 002 368

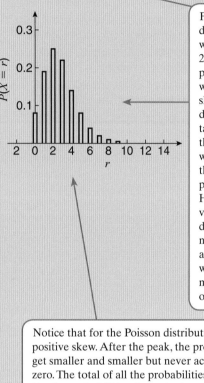

For a Poisson distribution with mean 2.6 the probabilities would be as shown in the diagram and table. Two or three cases would have the highest probabilities. However, for a very contagious disease, either no cases or a lot of cases will be the most likely outcomes.

Notice that for the Poisson distribution there is positive skew. After the peak, the probabilities get smaller and smaller but never actually get to zero. The total of all the probabilities will be 1. For the probabilities shown in the table, the total is 0.999 999 999 604.

Calculating Poisson probabilities

For a Poisson distribution, the average number of events in the given interval is a constant, λ; if X is the number of occurrences in the given interval, $X \sim$ Poisson (λ) shows that it has a Poisson distribution with mean λ.

The probability that X takes a value r is given by

$$P(X = r) = e^{-\lambda} \frac{\lambda^r}{r!} \text{ for } r = 0, 1, 2, 3, 4, \ldots$$

A ADVICE

e is the number 2.718 281 828… You should use the e^x button on your calculator when working with the Poisson probability formula.

EXAMPLE 2

Sweets are sold in tubes of mixed colours. On average, there are 3.6 blue sweets in a tube. Assume that the number of blue sweets in a tube has a Poisson distribution. Find the probability that there will be 5 blue sweets in a tube.

SOLUTION

Notice that the power of e is negative.

X = the number of blue sweets in a tube.

Saying what the letters stand for helps you to organise your work and the examiner to understand what you are doing.

$X \sim$ Poisson (3.6)

$P(X = r) = e^{-\lambda} \dfrac{\lambda^r}{r!}$

For this question, $\lambda = 3.6, r = 5.$

$P(X = 5) = e^{-3.6} \times \dfrac{3.6^5}{5!} = 0.138$ (3 s.f.)

A ADVICE

Make sure you can use your calculator to get the answer in Example 2. You will need to know how to work out e^x, powers and factorials on your calculator.

Once you have used the Poisson probability formula, you can work with the probabilities in the same way as you did in S1.

EXAMPLE 3

Eloise buys two tubes of the sweets described in Example 2. What is the probability that there are no blue sweets in either of them? You should assume that the number of blue sweets per tube is independent of the contents of other tubes.

SOLUTION

For one tube, $P(X = 0) = e^{-3.6} \times \dfrac{3.6^0}{0!} = 0.0273$ (3 s.f.)

$\lambda = 3.6, r = 0$

$P(\text{none, none}) = 0.0273 \times 0.0273 = (0.0273)^2$

Remember, for independent events, $P(A \cap B) = P(A)P(B)$.

It is quicker to write the rounded probability but keep the unrounded value (0.027 32...) on your calculator for the final stage of working.

$P(\text{none, none}) = 0.000\ 747$ (3 s.f.)

Mean and variance

If X has a Poisson distribution then $E(X) = \text{Var}(X) = \lambda$. If the mean and variance are not the same, it cannot be a Poisson distribution. This fact is used when modelling with a Poisson distribution.

Sometimes you will have to work with more than one time interval in a question. You need to read the question carefully to make sure you are working out what is asked for.

EXAMPLE 4

A business hires out a carpet shampooing machine. The number of people wanting to hire the machine per day follows a Poisson distribution with mean 0.8.

i) Find the mean number of people wanting to hire the machine in a 5 day working week.

ii) What is the probability that exactly 5 people want to hire the machine in a working week?

SOLUTION

i) Mean number in 5 days is $5 \times 0.8 = 4$. ← 0.8 people per day on average for 5 days.

ii) X = the number of people wanting the machine in a week.

$X \sim$ Poisson (4)

$$P(X = r) = e^{-\lambda} \frac{\lambda^r}{r!}$$ ← For this question, $\lambda = 4, r = 5$.

$$P(X = 5) = e^{-4} \times \frac{4^5}{5!} = 0.156 \text{ (3 s.f.)}$$

LINKS

Pure Mathematics   The Exponential Function, e^x (C3).

Statistics   The Normal Distribution (S2).

Test Yourself

1 $X \sim$ Poisson(1.2). Three of the following statements are false and one is true. Find the one that is true.

A To find the mean you need to find the probability of each value then use the formula $E(X) = \sum r \, P(X = r)$.

B The probabilities for all the possible values of X add up to 1.

C $P(X = r) = e^{-1.2} \times \frac{1.2^r}{r}$.

D The standard deviation is 1.2.

This information is for questions 2 and 3.
X is the number of times a photocopier breaks down in a week.
X has a Poisson distribution with mean 2.8.

2 What is the probability that the photocopier breaks down exactly 5 times in a week? (Answers given to 3 s.f.)

  A 0.0459   **B** 0.0538   **C** 0.0872   **D** 0.935   **E** 1.50

3 What is the probability that the photocopier breaks down at least 3 times in a week? (Answers given to 3 s.f.)

  A 0.222   **B** 0.308   **C** 0.530   **D** 0.531   **E** 0.692

4 The Reds are playing The Blues at football. You can assume that, for each team, the number of goals they score will have a Poisson distribution. The mean number of goals per game for The Reds is 1.2 and for The Blues it is 1.6. The teams' scores are independent of each other. What is the probability that The Reds win 1–0? (Answers given to 3 s.f.)

  A 0   **B** 0.073   **C** 0.097   **D** 0.170   **E** 0.563

5 As part of biology field work, a group of students calculates that the mean number of daisies per m² in a field is 3.7. Assume that the number of daisies in 1 m² has a Poisson distribution with mean 3.7. A student throws a quadrat of area 0.25 m² on to the field at random. What is the probability that there are no daisies in the quadrat?
(Answers given to 3 s.f.)

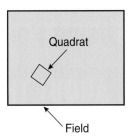

Quadrat

Field

  A 3.74×10^{-7} B 0.025   C 0.397   D 0.925

  E There is not enough information to work it out.

Exam-Style Question

Part of a manager's job is to deal with queries from his staff. The number of queries he receives per hour, during the working day, follows a Poisson distribution with mean 0.5.

i) Find the probability that he receives no queries between 9 am and 10 am.

ii) Find the probability that he receives no more than 3 queries between 11 am and noon.

iii) The manager's working day is 8 hours long. How many queries will he receive, on average, during a working day?

iv) Find the probability that he receives exactly one query during a working day.

Using Poisson probability tables

A ABOUT THIS TOPIC

Using the Poisson probability formula enables you to find the probability of one outcome quickly and accurately. As you saw in the last section, working out the probability of a range of values by finding individual probabilities and adding them can be time consuming and there is a lot of scope for errors. Cumulative Poisson probability tables allow you to work out the probability of a range of values quickly. They will be given to you in the exam. You can find a copy of the tables in the *Companion to Advanced Mathematics and Statistics*.

R REMEMBER

- If $X \sim$ Poisson(λ) then $E(X) = Var(X) = \lambda$.
- Using cumulative binomial probability tables from S1.
- $P(A') = 1 - P(A)$ where A' is the event *not A* from S1.

K KEY FACTS

- A discrete random variable may be modelled by a Poisson distribution if:
  - events occur at random and independently of each other
  - the average number of events in a given interval of time or space is a constant, λ.
- If X is the number of occurrences in the given interval then
  $P(X = r) = e^{-\lambda} \dfrac{\lambda^r}{r!}$ for $r = 0, 1, 2, 3, 4, \ldots$
- Cumulative Poisson probability tables give values of $P(X \leq x)$. This is the total probability
  $P(X = 0) + P(X = 1) + \ldots + P(X = x)$.

Using tables to find the total probability of a range of values

A ADVICE

The Poisson probability tables you get in the exam are cumulative probability tables. They tell you the sum of the individual probabilities up to and including the given number of occurrences, x, so they give you $P(X \leq x)$.

EXAMPLE 1

A car hire business finds that the number of customers who want to hire a car per day follows a Poisson distribution with mean 3.6. What is the probability that no more than 3 customers want to hire a car on a particular day?

SOLUTION

X = the number of customers who want to hire a car on a day.

> Remember to say what the letters you introduce stand for.

X has a Poisson distribution with mean 3.6.
You can write this as $X \sim$ Poisson (3.6).
You are asked to find $P(X \le 3)$.
You need to look in the section of the tables for $\lambda = 3.6$.
This gives you
$\qquad P(X \le 3) = 0.5152 = 0.515$ (3 d.p.)

> This column gives values of x so that you can read across to find $P(X \le x)$.

x \ λ	3.60
0	0.0273
1	0.1257
2	0.3027
3	0.5152
4	0.7064

A ADVICE

You can get the answer to Example 1 from tables directly. It helps to show the examiner what you are doing if you write that $\lambda = 3.6$ and that you want $P(X \le 3)$. This will also help you to keep track of what you are trying to do.

What if you want the probability of a range of values but it isn't in the form $P(X \le x)$?

You can use the cumulative Poisson probability tables to find many kinds of probabilities that involve a range of values.

EXAMPLE 2

$X \sim$ Poisson (8.1). Find $P(3 \le X < 8)$.

> Note that 8 is not included but 3 is.

SOLUTION

First think what values are possible for X.
X must be a whole number so possible values are $3, 4, 5, 6, 7$
These are the values that are less than or equal to 7 but without the values that are less than or equal to 2.
$P(3 \le X < 8) = P(X \le 7) - P(X \le 2)$
$P(3 \le X < 8) = 0.4391 - 0.0127 = 0.4264$
$P(3 \le X < 8) \approx 0.426$

> When you are doing calculations with numbers from 4-figure tables, your final answer will only be accurate to 3 decimal places so you should round it.

x \ λ	8.10
0	0.0003
1	0.0028
2	0.0127
3	0.0396
4	0.0940
5	0.1822
6	0.3013
7	0.4391

Remember tables can only give you $P(X \le x)$ so you need to have probabilities with 'less than or equal to' before you can use them.

Translating words to symbols

Be careful when writing the probability you want as an inequality. Some commonly used phrases, and how they translate to symbols, are listed in the table.

Phrase	Fewer than 3	No more than 3	Up to 3	More than 3	No fewer than 3	At least 3
Symbols	$X < 3$	$X \leqslant 3$	$X \leqslant 3$	$X > 3$	$X \geqslant 3$	$X \geqslant 3$
Values (X is an integer)	0, 1, 2	0, 1, 2, 3	0, 1, 2, 3	4, 5, 6, …	3, 4, 5, …	3, 4, 5, …

Remember that there is no maximum possible value for the number of occurrences, X, in a Poisson distribution, but the lowest possible value is zero.

EXAMPLE 3

Power cuts in a town occur with a mean of 1.1 per week. Assume that the number of power cuts in a week has a Poisson distribution. What is the probability that there will be at least 5 power cuts in a week?

SOLUTION

X = the number of power cuts in a week.

> Write down the value of λ; this will help you get the right part of the tables.

$X \sim$ Poisson (1.1) so $\lambda = 1.1$
$P(X \geqslant 5)$ is required.
Possible values of X are 5, 6, 7, 8, … , i.e. not 0 to 4.
$P(X \geqslant 5) = 1 - P(X \leqslant 4)$
$P(X \geqslant 5) = 1 - 0.9946 = 0.0054$
$P(X \geqslant 5) \approx 0.005$

x \ λ	1.00	1.10
0	0.3679	0.3329
1	0.7358	0.6990
2	0.9197	0.9004
3	0.9810	0.9743
4	0.9963	0.9946
5	0.9994	0.9990
6	0.9999	0.9999

Tables or graphical calculator?

Some graphical calculators will work out cumulative Poisson probabilities between two values. If you are using a graphical calculator instead of tables, you should still write down the value of λ. You should also write down the probability you are looking for: $P(X \geqslant 5)$ in Example 3.

$P(X \geqslant 5)$ means the total probability for X values 5, 6, 7, 8, 9, … There is no largest possible value. You only need the probability to 3 or 4 decimal places so you can find the probability that X is between 5 and some large number. Choose the large number carefully. If it is too small, your probability will be inaccurate. If it is very large, your calculator may take a long time to do the calculation.

A ADVICE

If you intend using a graphical calculator in the exam, practise using it when working through this section of the revision guide and make sure you can get the right answers.

A ADVICE

The examination specification for S2 includes use of cumulative Poisson probability tables. This means that you are expected to be able to use the tables. If you prefer to use a graphical calculator, you should make sure that you know how to use the tables as well. It is possible that a question could be asked which actually tells you to use the tables.

Deciding what inequality is needed

EXAMPLE 4

A car hire business has 4 cars for hire each day. The number of customers who want to hire a car per day follows a Poisson distribution with mean 3.6. What is the probability that, on a particular day, they have to turn customers away?

SOLUTION

They will have to turn customers away if more than 4 people want to hire a car.

$X \sim$ Poisson (3.6) where $X =$ the number of customers who want to hire a car on a day.

$P(X > 4)$ is needed.

X can be 5, 6, 7, 8, 9, ..., i.e. not 4 or less.

$P(X > 4) = 1 - P(X \leqslant 4) = 1 - 0.7064$

$P(X > 4) = 0.2936 \approx 0.294$

$x \backslash \lambda$	3.60
0	0.0273
1	0.1257
2	0.3027
3	0.5152
4	0.7064

LINKS

Statistics   The Normal Distribution (S2).

Test Yourself ▶L

1 X is a Poisson random variable. Four of the following statements about probability are true and one is false. Find the one that is false.

  A $P(X < 3) = P(X \leqslant 2)$

  B $P(3 \leqslant X \leqslant 6) = P(X \leqslant 6) - P(X \leqslant 3)$

  C $P(X \geqslant 7) = 1 - P(X \leqslant 6)$

  D $P(X > 8) = 1 - P(X \leqslant 8)$

  E $P(2 < X < 9) = P(X \leqslant 8) - P(X \leqslant 2)$

2 $X \sim$ Poisson (9.3). What is $P(X \geqslant 4)$? (Answers are given to 3 s.f.)

  A 0.0172

  B 0.0456

  C 0.901

  D 0.954

  E 0.983

This information is for questions 3 and 4.
There is a set of traffic lights on the road into a town. Outside peak hours, the number of vehicles arriving at these lights every minute can be modelled by a Poisson distribution with mean 2.3.

3 What is the probability that the number of cars arriving in 1 minute is more than 2 but fewer than 6? (Answers are given to 3 d.p.)

   A 0.374   B 0.392   C 0.395   D 0.639   E 0.660

4 There is time for 6 cars to go through the lights when they change. What is the probability that more than 6 cars arrive at the lights in an interval of 3 minutes? (Answers are given to 3 d.p.)

   A 0.009   B 0.404   C 0.465   D 0.535   E 0.686

5 The firemen on duty at night at a particular fire station know that the mean number of calls per night is 2.1. Assume that the number of calls per night follows a Poisson distribution with mean 2.1. What is the probability that there are more than 2 calls per night on each of 5 consecutive nights? (Answers are given to 3 s.f.)

   A 0.005 28   B 0.0919   C 0.116   D 0.350   E 0.603

Exam-Style Question ⊃L

A football supporter checks the statistics for his team and the opposing team they will play next weekend. He finds that his team score, on average, 1.1 goals per game and the opposing team score, on average, 1.4 goals.

i)   State two assumptions that are necessary for the Poisson distribution to provide a suitable model for the number of goals scored by a team in a game. Comment on whether these are likely to be valid.

For the rest of this question, assume that the number of goals scored by each team does indeed follow a Poisson distribution. Assume also that the number of goals each team scores is independent of the number of goals scored by the other team. Find the probability that:

ii) The opposing team scores 2 goals, or fewer, in the game.

iii) The supporter's team scores more than 2 goals in the game.

iv) The opposing team does not score but the supporter's team scores at least 1 goal.

Modelling using a Poisson distribution

A ABOUT THIS TOPIC

You have already seen examples of Poisson distributions being used for situations from life in the two previous sections. In this section you will compare theoretical results from using Poisson probability to what actually happened. When using statistical models to make predictions, it is important to compare the predictions to real life.

R REMEMBER

- For a Poisson distribution with X being the number of occurrences in an interval of given length
  $$P(X = r) = e^{-\lambda}\frac{\lambda^r}{r!}$$
  for $r = 0, 1, 2, 3, 4, \ldots$
- Cumulative Poisson probability tables give values of $P(X \leqslant x)$. This is the total probability $P(X = 0) + P(X = 1) + \ldots + P(X = x)$.
- $P(A') = 1 - P(A)$ where A' is the event *not A* from S1.
- Finding mean and variance from a frequency table from S1.
- The expectation of a binomial random variable is $E(X) = np$ from S1.

K KEY FACTS

- A discrete random variable may be modelled by a Poisson distribution if:
  - events occur at random, independently of each other, over an interval of time or space
  - the average number of events in the given interval is a constant, λ.
- If $X \sim \text{Poisson}(\lambda)$ then $E(X) = \text{Var}(X) = \lambda$.

When can you use a Poisson distribution?

As you have seen in previous sections, a discrete random variable may be modelled by a Poisson distribution if:
- events occur at random, independently of each other, over an interval of time or space
- the average number of events in the given interval is a constant, λ.

EXAMPLE 1

Thirty students each choose 1 m² of a field at random and count the number of daisy plants in it. Assume the number of daisies per m² follows a Poisson distribution with mean 3.9.

i) How many of the students would be expected to get a count of 3 daisies?

ii) How many of the students would be expected to get a count of more than 5 daisies?

SOLUTION

X = the number of daisies in 1 m².

$X \sim$ Poisson (3.9) so $P(X = r) = e^{-\lambda} \dfrac{\lambda^r}{r!}$ with $\lambda = 3.9$.

> Don't round this as it is not the final answer.

i) $P(X = 3) = e^{-3.9} \times \dfrac{3.9^3}{3!} = 0.2001\ldots$

Each of the 30 students has the same probability of finding 3 daisies so the number of students who get 3 daisies is binomially distributed.

Remember from S1, the expectation of a binomial random variable is $E(X) = np$.

The expected number of students who count 3 daisies is
$30 \times 0.2001\ldots = 6.0036\ldots \approx 6.0$

> Round the answer sensibly; the expected number of students need not always be a whole number. Remember the expected number is an average.

A ADVICE

Don't worry if you find it confusing that the number of daisies in 1 m² has a Poisson distribution but the number of students out of 30 who would count 3 daisies has a binomial distribution.
A probability of 0.2001… is around 1 in 5 students. If 1 in every 5 students see 3 daisies, then for 30 students, we would expect 6 of them to do so.

ii) First work out $P(X > 5)$.

Possible values are 6, 7, 8, 9, 10, … , i.e. not 5 or less.

$P(X > 5) = 1 - P(X \leqslant 5)$

$P(X > 5) = 1 - 0.8006 = 0.1994$

Expected number of students with more than 5 daisies is
$30 \times 0.1994 = 5.982 \approx 6.0$.

x \ λ	3.90
0	0.0202
1	0.0992
2	0.2531
3	0.4532
4	0.6484
5	0.8006

Mean and variance

You already know that if $X \sim$ Poisson(λ) then $E(X) = Var(X) = \lambda$. The mean and variance of a Poisson distribution are equal. Working out the mean and variance of a set of data is one way of checking whether a Poisson distribution might be suitable.

> ⚠ If the mean and variance of a set of data are equal, this does not mean that they must come from a Poisson distribution but if the mean and variance are very different, it indicates that they do not.

EXAMPLE 2

The results of the daisy counting experiment described in Example 1 are shown in the table.

Number of daisies	0	1	2	3	4	5	6	More than 6
Frequency	1	2	2	6	7	7	5	0

i) Calculate the sample mean and the sample variance.

ii) Comment on whether or not your results confirm that the number of daisies per m² has a Poisson distribution.

SOLUTION

i) Remember the mean is $\bar{x} = \dfrac{\sum xf}{n}$ so

$$\bar{x} = \frac{117}{30} = 3.9$$

Variance is $s^2 = \dfrac{S_{xx}}{n-1}$ where

$$S_{xx} = \sum x^2 f - n\bar{x}^2 = 531 - 30 \times 3.9^2$$

$$= 74.7$$

$$s^2 = \frac{74.7}{29} = 2.5758\ldots \approx 2.58$$

ii) The sample mean and variance are not nearly equal. This suggests that a Poisson distribution may not be a suitable model.

Number of daisies, x	Frequency, f	xf	x^2f
0	1	0	0
1	2	2	2
2	2	4	8
3	6	18	54
4	7	28	112
5	7	35	175
6	5	30	180
Total	30	117	531

You don't need the 'more than 6' row as it had no frequency so did not happen.

A ADVICE

You may sometimes be told the sample mean and/or variance in a question. If Example 2 asked you 'Show that the sample mean is 3.9', you would still have to work it out but if it just said 'The sample mean is 3.9, calculate the variance' then you would not need to work out the mean.

⚠ You might be told the standard deviation in a question. Remember the mean and **variance** are equal for a Poisson distribution. The standard deviation, $s = \sqrt{\text{variance}}$. If you are told the standard deviation, square it to get the variance.

Comparing model and reality

Expected frequency can be used to compare the predictions of the Poisson model with actual data. Look back at Example 1 for a reminder of how to calculate expected frequency.

EXAMPLE 3

Over many years, statistics classes have collected data on the number of cars passing the school in 15 second periods. The results have shown that a Poisson distribution with mean 2 is a suitable model for the number of cars passing the school in 15 seconds during the school day.

i) Use the Poisson model to find the probability that there are more than 4 cars in a 15 second period.

ii) A member of staff surveys traffic passing the school between 8.00 and 8.15 in the morning. He counts the number of cars passing the school in each of the 15 second periods. There are more than 4 cars in 14 of the 60 periods. Why does your answer to **(i)** suggest that the Poisson model with mean 2 is not appropriate? Give a reason why the model may not be appropriate for this time of day.

SOLUTION

X = the number of cars in 15 seconds.
$X \sim$ Poisson (2)

i) $P(X > 4) = 1 - P(X \leq 4)$

Possible values are $5, 6, 7, 8, \ldots$, i.e. not 4 or less.

$P(X > 4) = 1 - 0.9473 = 0.0527$

$x \backslash^{\lambda}$	2.00
0	0.1353
1	0.4060
2	0.6767
3	0.8571
4	0.9473

ii) If the Poisson model with mean 2 was still appropriate, the expected number of periods with more than 4 cars would be $60 \times 0.0527 = 3.162$.

> You were told there are 60 time periods.

14 is much more than this so this suggests the model is not appropriate.
The time period 8.00 am to 8.15 am could be a much busier time of day than during the school day.

LINKS

Statistics   Statistical Modelling (S1–S4);
χ^2 Test for Goodness of Fit (S3).

Test Yourself ⅄L

These data are for questions 1 and 2.
The number of radioactive particles decaying in 520 time intervals of 10 seconds is shown:

Number of particles counted in 10 second interval	0	1	2	3	4	5	6	7	8	9	10
Frequency	11	39	83	104	106	82	47	30	10	5	3

1 Find the mean and variance of these data. (Rounded answers are given to 2 d.p.)
   A The mean is 3.84, the variance is 3.62.   **B** The mean is 3.84, the variance is 3.63.
   C The mean is 3.84, the variance is 3.65.   **D** The mean is 5, the variance is 11.

Make sure you have got the right mean and variance for question 1 before doing question 2.

2 Four of the statements below are false and one is true. Find the one that is true.
   A The mean and variance are equal so the data must be from a Poisson distribution.
   B The mean and variance are close so the data must be from a Poisson distribution.
   C The mean and variance are not equal so the data can't be from a Poisson distribution.
   D The mean and standard deviation are not equal so the data can't be from a Poisson distribution.
   E The mean and variance are close so the data could be from a Poisson distribution.

3 The number of emails received by a customer contact centre is believed to follow a Poisson distribution with a mean of 12 per hour during work time. The number of emails received each hour during work time is observed for 36 hours. What is the expected frequency of 10 emails in an hour?
   A 0   **B** 0.1 (1 d.p)   **C** 3   **D** 3.8 (1 d.p.)   **E** 12

4 The number of telephone calls a helpline receives in work time is believed to follow a Poisson distribution with mean 5.4 per hour. The number of telephone calls received each hour during work time is observed for 36 hours. What is the expected frequency of 8 or more telephone calls in an hour? (All answers to 1 d.p.)
   A 0.2   **B** 2.9   **C** 3.5   **D** 6.4   **E** 32.5

Exam-Style Question ▶L

A random sample of word processed pages produced by a new secretary is being proofread. The random variable X denotes the number of errors per page.

i) State two assumptions that are necessary for the Poisson distribution to provide a suitable model for the distribution of X. Comment on whether these are likely to be valid.

The data in the table show the results of proofreading a random sample of 50 pages.

x	0	1	2	3	4	>4
Frequency, f	16	20	10	3	1	0

ii) Calculate the sample mean and the sample variance.

iii) Do the results of your calculations in part ii) support the suggestion that the Poisson distribution is a suitable model for the distribution of X? Explain your answer.

iv) Assume that X may be modelled by a Poisson distribution with mean 1.1. Find the probability that a 10-page document produced by the secretary will contain no errors.

The sum of two or more Poisson distributions

A ABOUT THIS TOPIC

Suppose it is known that, on average, 4.2 female drivers and 6.1 male drivers join a road per minute. It comes as no surprise that, on average, 10.3 drivers altogether join the road per minute. However, if the distributions of the number of female drivers and the number of male drivers are independent Poisson distributions, then the distribution of the total number of drivers also has a Poisson distribution. This idea is useful for working out probabilities.

R REMEMBER

- X is the number of occurrences in an interval of given length.
  - If $X \sim \text{Poisson}(\lambda)$ then $E(X) = \text{Var}(X) = \lambda$
  - and $P(X = r) = e^{-\lambda}\dfrac{\lambda^r}{r!}$ for $r = 0, 1, 2, 3, 4, \ldots$
- Cumulative Poisson probability tables give values of $P(X \leqslant x)$. This is the total probability $P(X = 0) + P(X = 1) + \ldots + P(X = x)$.
- Probability from S1.

K KEY FACTS

- The sum of two **independent** Poisson distributions also has a Poisson distribution.
  If $X \sim \text{Poisson}(\lambda)$ and $Y \sim \text{Poisson}(\mu)$ then $X + Y \sim \text{Poisson}(\lambda + \mu)$.

Simplifying calculations

On average, 4.2 female drivers and 6.1 male drivers join a road per minute. The distributions of the number of female drivers and the number of male drivers are independent Poisson distributions. It would be possible to find the probability that exactly one driver joins the road in a minute by realising that it must be one of the following possibilities:
- one female driver and no male drivers
OR
- no female drivers and one male driver.

Number of female drivers, F	$F \sim \text{Poisson }(4.2)$	$P(F = 0) = e^{-4.2} \times \dfrac{4.2^0}{0!}$ $= 0.014995\ldots$	$P(F = 1) = e^{-4.2} \times \dfrac{4.2^1}{1!}$ $= 0.062981\ldots$
Number of male drivers, M	$M \sim \text{Poisson }(6.1)$	$P(M = 0) = e^{-6.1} \times \dfrac{6.1^0}{0!}$ $= 0.0022428\ldots$	$P(M = 1) = e^{-6.1} \times \dfrac{6.1^1}{1!}$ $= 0.013681\ldots$

$P(\text{1 driver}) = P(F = 0) \times P(M = 1) + P(F = 1) \times P(M = 0)$

$P(\text{1 driver}) = 0.014995\ldots \times 0.013681\ldots + 0.062981\ldots \times 0.0022428\ldots$
$= 0.000346 \text{ (to 3 s.f.)}$

> The number of female drivers is independent of the number of male drivers, so to work out the probability of no female drivers and one male driver, you multiply the separate probabilities.

It is much quicker to use the fact that the total number of drivers has a Poisson distribution with mean $4.2 + 6.1 = 10.3$.

$P(\text{1 driver}) = e^{-10.3} \times \dfrac{10.3^1}{1!} = 0.000346 \text{ (3 s.f.)}$

The sum of two independent Poisson distributions also has a Poisson distribution.
If $X \sim \text{Poisson}(\lambda)$ and $Y \sim \text{Poisson}(\mu)$ then $X + Y \sim \text{Poisson}(\lambda + \mu)$.
This principle also works for more than two independent Poisson distributions.

The Poisson distribution

EXAMPLE 1

A post office has two windows for customer service. One window is for customers who only want stamps. The number of customers arriving at this window in a 5-minute interval has a Poisson distribution with mean 1.8. The second window is for customers who want other services. The number of customers arriving at the second window in a 5-minute interval has a Poisson distribution with mean 2.3. Both sets of customers arrive independently of each other. What is the probability that the total number of customers in a 5-minute interval exceeds 6?

SOLUTION

X = the number of customers arriving at the first window in 5 minutes.

Y = the number of customers arriving at the second window in 5 minutes.

> Summarise the information in the question. Make sure you say what the letters stand for.

$X \sim$ Poisson (1.8) $Y \sim$ Poisson (2.3)   so $X + Y \sim$ Poisson (4.1)

$P(X + Y) > 6 = 1 - P(X + Y \leqslant 6)$

> X and Y are independent so their sum has a Poisson distribution.

> Possible values are 7, 8, 9, 10, ... , i.e. not 0 to 6.

> ⚠ You can only assume that the sum of two Poisson distributions has a Poisson distribution if the two original distributions are independent.

$P(X + Y) > 6 = 1 - 0.8786$

$P(X + Y) > 6 = 0.1214 \approx 0.121$

x \ λ	4.00	4.10
0	0.0183	0.0166
1	0.0916	0.0845
2	0.2381	0.2238
3	0.4335	0.4142
4	0.6288	0.6093
5	0.7851	0.7693
6	0.8893	0.8786

Remember all the usual ways of working with Poisson distributions.

EXAMPLE 2

For the situation described in Example 1, what is the probability that the total number of customers is zero in a 1-minute interval?

SOLUTION

The total number of customers in 5 minutes has a mean of 4.1.
The mean in 1 minute is $4.1 \div 5 = 0.82$.
T = the total number of customers in a 1-minute interval.
$T \sim$ Poisson (0.82)

> If the number of customers in 5 minutes has a Poisson distribution then so does the number of customers in 1 minute. The mean is different but the type of distribution is not.

$P(T = r) = e^{-\lambda} \dfrac{\lambda^r}{r!}$ $\lambda = 0.82$ and $r = 0$

$P(T = 0) = e^{-0.82} \times \dfrac{0.82^0}{0!} = e^{-0.82} = 0.4404... \approx 0.44$

The sum of any number of independent Poisson distributions has a Poisson distribution.

EXAMPLE 3

A café monitors the number of different types of hot drinks sold in a 5-minute interval. They sell tea, coffee and hot chocolate. In a 5-minute interval, the number of cups of tea has a Poisson distribution with mean 3.1, the number of cups of coffee has a Poisson distribution with mean 4.3 and the number of cups of hot chocolate has a Poisson distribution with mean 0.8. The Poisson distributions may be assumed to be independent.

i) Calculate the probability that, in a given 5-minute interval, exactly no cups of tea, 6 cups of coffee and no cups of hot chocolate are sold.

ii) Calculate the probability that, in a given 5-minute interval, 10 or more hot drinks are sold.

iii) In a given 5-minute interval, exactly 6 hot drinks are sold. Find the probability that they are all coffee.

SOLUTION

T = the number of cups of tea sold in 5 minutes
C = the number of cups of coffee sold in 5 minutes
H = the number of cups of hot chocolate sold in 5 minutes
D = the total number of hot drinks sold in 5 minutes.

> Write down what all the letters you use stand for. It is very easy to lose track of what you are doing in a question like this.

$T \sim$ Poisson (3.1) $C \sim$ Poisson (4.3) $H \sim$ Poisson (0.8) $D \sim$ Poisson (8.2)

> This part of the question is about the distributions of individual drinks. The distributions are independent so you can multiply the probabilities to find the overall probability.

> The distributions are independent and 3.1 + 4.3 + 0.8 = 8.2.

i) $P(T = 0 \ \& \ C = 6 \ \& \ H = 0) = P(T = 0) \times P(C = 6) \times P(H = 0)$

$P(T = 0 \ \& \ C = 6 \ \& \ H = 0) = e^{-3.1} \times \dfrac{3.1^0}{0!} \times e^{-4.3} \times \dfrac{4.3^6}{6!} \times e^{-0.8} \times \dfrac{0.8^0}{0!}$

$P(T = 0 \ \& \ C = 6 \ \& \ H = 0) = 0.0450\ldots \times 0.1191\ldots \times 0.4493\ldots$
$= 0.0024\ldots \approx 0.002$

ii) $P(D \geqslant 10) = 1 - P(D \leqslant 9)$
To find the probability of 10 or more drinks (10, 11, 12, 13, …) you need 'not 9 or fewer'.
$P(D \geqslant 10) = 1 - 0.6915 = 0.3085$

x $\diagdown$ λ	8.20
7	0.4254
8	0.5647
9	0.6915
10	0.7955

iii) $P(C = 6 \mid D = 6)$

> This part of the question uses conditional probability. You know that 6 hot drinks are sold and you want to know the probability that there are 6 coffees sold.

> Remember conditional probability from S1: $P(A \mid B) = \dfrac{P(A \cap B)}{P(B)}$ where $A \cap B$ is the event 'A and B'.

$$P(C = 6 \mid D = 6) = \frac{P([C = 6] \cap [D = 6])}{P(D = 6)} = \frac{P(C = 6, T = 0, H = 0)}{P(D = 6)}$$

> If there are 6 coffees and 6 hot drinks in total; this means 6 coffees, no teas and no hot chocolates. This is the probability you worked out in part **i)**; you will need to use the unrounded value in part **iii)**.

$$P(D = 6) = e^{-8.2} \times \frac{8.2^6}{6!} = 0.1159\ldots$$

$$P(C = 6 \mid D = 6) = \frac{0.0024\ldots}{0.1159\ldots} = 0.0207\ldots \approx 0.021.$$

LINKS

Statistics   Linear combinations of independent Normal random variables (S3).

Test Yourself ⊃L

This information is for questions 1 and 2.
An office has two printers. The number of times the first printer jams in a working week has a Poisson distribution with mean 1.3. The number of times the second printer jams in a working week has a Poisson distribution with mean 0.6. The two distributions may be assumed to be independent.

1 Find the probability that the total number of printer jams in a given week exceeds 3. (Probabilities are given to 3 d.p.)

   A 0.046   B 0.125   C 0.171   D 0.296   E 0.875

2 There are 5 days in a working week. Find the probability that there is at least one printer jam in a given day. (Probabilities are given to 2 d.p.)

   A 0.26   B 0.32   C 0.34   D 0.68   E 0.85

This information is for questions 3, 4 and 5.
A manager in a business receives two kinds of emails: internal (from inside the business) and external (from outside the business). The number of internal emails in 15 minutes can be modelled by a Poisson distribution with mean 1.4. The number of external emails in 15 minutes can be modelled by a Poisson distribution with mean 2.7. Both types of email arrive independently of each other.

3 Find the probability that the manager receives at least one email of each type in a given 15-minute interval. (Probabilities are given to 3 d.p.)

   A 0.063   B 0.703   C 0.915   D 0.983   E 1.686

4 Find the probability that the manager receives exactly 10 emails in a given half-hour interval. (Probabilities are given to 3 d.p.)

   A 0.006   B 0.027   C 0.104   D 0.160   E 0.796

5 Given that the manager receives exactly 10 emails in half an hour, find the probability that they are all external emails. (Probabilities are given to 3 d.p.)

   A 0.001   B 0.002   C 0.015   D 0.019   E 0.252

Exam-Style Question ⊃L

Customers of a takeaway can either collect the food themselves or ask for it to be delivered. The number of orders received per half-hour for collection can be assumed to be a Poisson variable with mean 6.3. The number of orders received per half-hour for delivery can be assumed to be an independent Poisson variable with mean 3.5.

i)   Calculate the probability that in a given half-hour exactly 5 orders for delivery are received.

ii) Calculate the probability that in a given half-hour exactly 20 orders are received altogether.

iii) Calculate the probability that in a given 15-minute interval more than 12 orders are received altogether.

The Poisson approximation to the binomial distribution

A ABOUT THIS TOPIC

In S1 you used the binomial distribution for situations where an experiment is conducted a fixed number of times and the probability of 'success' each time is the same. If this probability is small and the experiment is conducted many times, the probabilities can be calculated by using an approximate Poisson distribution; this simplifies the calculations.

R REMEMBER

- $X \sim B(n, p)$ means that X has a binomial distribution with n repetitions of the experiment; p is the probability of 'success' each time.
- For a binomial random variable, $P(X = r) = {}^nC_r q^{n-r} p^r$ where $q = 1 - p$, $r = 0, 1, 2, ..., n$.
- The expectation of a binomial random variable is $E(X) = np$.
- If $X \sim \text{Poisson}(\lambda)$ then $E(X) = \text{Var}(X) = \lambda$.
- The formula for calculating probabilities for a Poisson random variable is $P(X = r) = e^{-\lambda} \dfrac{\lambda^r}{r!}$ for $r = 0, 1, 2, 3, 4, ...$

K KEY FACTS

- The Poisson distribution may be used as an approximation to the binomial distribution if, for $X \sim B(n, p)$,
  - n is large
  - p is small (i.e. a rare event)
  - np is not too large (typically, no more than 10).
- For the approximating Poisson distribution, $\lambda = np$.

EXAMPLE 1

The probability of winning any prize in the UK national lottery is about $\frac{1}{54}$. For this question, assume that the probability of winning a prize is exactly $\frac{1}{54}$. Fiona buys two tickets a week for 52 weeks (1 year). What is the probability that she wins at least one prize?

SOLUTION

To find the probability of winning at least once, first work out the probability of losing every time.

P(lose once) $= 1 - \frac{1}{54} = \frac{53}{54}$

Number of tickets bought $= 2 \times 52 = 104$

P(lose every time) $= \frac{53}{54} \times \frac{53}{54} \times \frac{53}{54} \times ... \frac{53}{54} = \left(\frac{53}{54}\right)^{104} = 0.1431...$

> Each game is independent so the probability of lose and lose and ... and lose is found by multiplying the individual probabilities.

P(win at least once) $= 1 - $ P(lose every time)
$= 1 - 0.1431... = 0.8568...$

The probability of winning at least once is 0.857 (to 3 d.p.)

For the situation in Example 1, the number of wins in a year has a binomial distribution. There are 104 tickets bought and each time the probability of winning is the same ($\frac{1}{54}$). The calculations involved in working out the probabilities can be simplified by using the Poisson approximation to the binomial distribution.

For Example 1, $n = 104$, $p = \frac{1}{54}$, so the mean is $\lambda = np$,
i.e. $\lambda = 104 \times \frac{1}{54} = \frac{52}{27}$.

The Poisson distribution may be used as an approximation to the binomial distribution if, for $X \sim B(n, p)$,
- n is large (in this case $n = 104$)
- p is small (i.e. a rare event) (in this case $p = \frac{1}{54}$)
- np is not too large (typically, no more than 10) (in this case $np \approx 1.926$).

The mean of the approximating Poisson distribution is the same as that for the binomial distribution so $\lambda = np$.

The table and diagram show probabilities calculated using $B(104, \frac{1}{54})$ and Poisson$(\frac{52}{27})$. You can see they are quite close.

Value (r)	Probability (p)	
	B $(104, \frac{1}{54})$	Poisson $(\frac{52}{27})$
0	0.1431	0.1457
1	0.2809	0.2807
2	0.2729	0.2703
3	0.1751	0.1735
4	0.08341	0.08355
5	0.03148	0.03218
6	0.009799	0.01033
7	0.002588	0.002842

Comparison of $B(104, \frac{1}{54})$ and Poisson $(\frac{52}{27})$

- Binomial distribution
- Poisson distribution

EXAMPLE 2

A study finds that 1.5% of children in an area have nut allergies. A school in this area has 500 students.

i) What is the expected number of students in the school with nut allergies, assuming that they are a random sample from the population?

ii) Assume that a binomial distribution is appropriate and use a suitable approximating distribution to calculate the probability that the school will have more than 5 students with nut allergies.

SOLUTION

i) The probability of a student chosen at random having a nut allergy is 1.5% = 0.015.
The number of students is 500.
$p = 0.015$, $n = 500$
Expected number = $np = 500 \times 0.015 = 7.5$.

ii) Since n is large and p is small, the Poisson approximation is appropriate.
X = number of students with nut allergies at the school.
$X \sim$ Poisson (7.5) (approximately).
$P(X > 5) = 1 - P(X \leqslant 5)$
Possible values are 6, 7, 8, 9, ... , i.e. not 5 or fewer.

$P(X > 5) = 1 - 0.2414$

$P(X > 5) = 0.7586$
The probability that the school has more than 5 students with nut allergies is 0.759 (to 3 d.p.).

$x \backslash ^{\lambda}$	7.50
0	0.0006
1	0.0047
2	0.0203
3	0.0591
4	0.1321
5	0.2414
6	0.3782

A ADVICE

Poisson probability tables can be used in the last part once the probability has been changed round to have 'less than or equal to' in it.

Note: The assumption in this solution is that the probability for students in the school is the same as for children in the area and that cases are independent of each other. If allergies tend to run in families and there are several children from nut allergy prone families at the school, then this may not be the case.

EXAMPLE 3

A rail company keeps data about the train journeys it runs. For one rail line, 2% of trains are late. Each train is equally likely to be late. There are 50 trains on this line each week.

i) State the distribution of X, the number of late trains in a week on this line.

Use a suitable approximating distribution to find the probability that, for this line:

ii) In 1 week, there will be exactly 2 late trains.

iii) In 2 weeks, there will be at least 5 late trains.

SOLUTION

i) $X \sim$ B (50, 0.02) ← Each train has the same probability of being late (2% = 0.02). There are 50 trains a week.

ii) $p = 0.02, n = 50$, so $\lambda = 50 \times 0.02 = 1$

$X \sim$ Poisson (1) (approximately) n is large and p is small so the Poisson approximation can be used.

$P(X = r) = e^{-\lambda} \dfrac{\lambda^r}{r!}$

Substituting $r = 2$ gives:

$P(X = 2) = e^{-1} \times \dfrac{1^2}{2!} = 0.1839...$

The probability that there will be exactly 2 late trains in a week is 0.184 (to 3 d.p.).

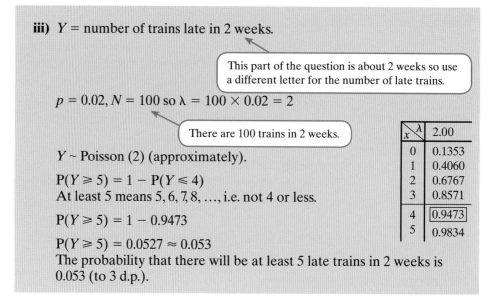

iii) Y = number of trains late in 2 weeks.

> This part of the question is about 2 weeks so use a different letter for the number of late trains.

$p = 0.02, N = 100$ so $\lambda = 100 \times 0.02 = 2$

> There are 100 trains in 2 weeks.

$Y \sim$ Poisson (2) (approximately).

$P(Y \geqslant 5) = 1 - P(Y \leqslant 4)$
At least 5 means 5, 6, 7, 8, ..., i.e. not 4 or less.

$P(Y \geqslant 5) = 1 - 0.9473$

$P(Y \geqslant 5) = 0.0527 \approx 0.053$
The probability that there will be at least 5 late trains in 2 weeks is 0.053 (to 3 d.p.).

x \ λ	2.00
0	0.1353
1	0.4060
2	0.6767
3	0.8571
4	0.9473
5	0.9834

LINKS

Statistics   Normal approximations to binomial and Poisson distributions (S2).

Test Yourself ⊃L

1 Of the people in a city, 3% have blood type AB. 100 people go to give blood at a blood donor session. Assume these people are a random sample from the city population. Four of the following statements are true and one is false. Find the one that is false.
   A There will be 3 people with blood type AB.
   B The probability that a person chosen at random from the population has blood type AB is 0.03.
   C The number of people with blood type AB at a blood donor session is binomially distributed.
   D The probability that there are no people with blood type AB at a blood donor session is around 5%.
   E The number of people with blood type AB at a blood donor session has an approximate Poisson distribution with mean 3.

This information is for questions 2 and 3.
A supermarket gives a 'lucky shopper' discount to some customers. A letter from the alphabet is chosen at random after the bill has been added up. Each letter in the alphabet has the same chance of being chosen. If the letter matches the first letter of the customer's surname, the bill is reduced by 5%. A customer shops at the supermarket every week for 1 year (52 weeks).

2 Use a suitable approximate distribution to find the probability that a customer has the bill reduced 5 times during the year. (Probabilities are given to 3 d.p.)
   A 0.036   B 0.074   C 0.084   D 0.192   E 0.983

3 Use a suitable approximate distribution to find the probability that a customer has the bill reduced at least 3 times during the year. (Probabilities are given to 3 d.p.)
   A 0.143   B 0.180   C 0.323   D 0.677   E 0.857

4 Of the drawing pins produced at a factory, 0.1% are faulty. The drawing pins are packed in boxes of 500. A customer buys two boxes. You should assume that faulty pins are well-mixed with pins that are alright. Use an approximate method to find the probability that there is more than one faulty drawing pin in each of the boxes. (Probabilities are given to 3 d.p.)
   A 0.008   B 0.080   C 0.090   D 0.180   E 0.921

5 Tess uses a spreadsheet to compare probabilities for the distributions $X \sim B(75, 0.08)$ and $X \sim$ Poisson (6). She finds that, in this case, there is over 50% error in the value of $P(X = 15)$ found by using the Poisson approximation compared to the value found by using the binomial distribution. Which is the correct reason for this percentage error being so large?

A n is too small to use the Poisson approximation to the binomial.

B p is too large to use the Poisson approximation to the binomial.

C np is too large to use the Poisson approximation to the binomial.

D The two distributions have different means.

E The probability of X being 15 is so small that a slight difference in values means a large percentage error.

Exam-Style Question ⟩L

An airline finds that, on average, 5% of people who book a seat fail to turn up for the flight.

i) If 142 bookings are taken for a flight, how many people, on average, will fail to turn up?

ii) State the conditions under which a Poisson distribution is appropriate as an approximation to the binomial distribution.

142 bookings have been taken for a flight.

iii) The aeroplane has 136 seats. Use a suitable Poisson approximating distribution to find the probability that more than 136 people turn up for the flight.

The Normal distribution

▶▶ 34
44
49
50
52

Using Normal probability tables

A ABOUT THIS TOPIC

The Normal probability distribution is used to describe measurements of many naturally occurring variables such as human height or leaf length. It is also widely used as an approximating distribution. If you study or work in medical, biological or social sciences you will use the Normal distribution.

R REMEMBER

- If the variables x and y are related by $y = a + bx$ (a and b constant) then the means are related by
  $\bar{y} = a + b\bar{x}$ and
  the standard deviations are related by
  $s_y = bs_x$. (S1).
- The probability you learnt in S1.

K KEY FACTS

- If a random variable, X, has a Normal distribution with mean μ and standard deviation σ, this can be written as $X \sim N(\mu, \sigma^2)$.

- Standard Normal tables are for a Normal distribution with mean 0 and standard deviation 1. A variable with this distribution is often given the symbol Z. $Z \sim N(0, 1)$.

- Standard Normal tables give the probability that Z is less than a particular value (z). This is represented by the shaded area in the diagram.

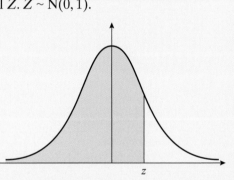

- The total area under the Normal curve is 1.

- To use standard Normal tables, other Normal variables have to be standardised by subtracting the mean and then dividing by the standard deviation: $z = \dfrac{x - \mu}{\sigma}$.

What is the Normal distribution?

The Normal distribution is a theoretical distribution which can be used for many naturally occurring variables. $N(\mu, \sigma^2)$ stands for the Normal distribution with mean μ and standard deviation σ (variance σ^2). The standard Normal distribution, $N(0, 1)$, has mean 0 and variance 1. A Normal distribution has a bell-shaped curve as shown in the diagram.

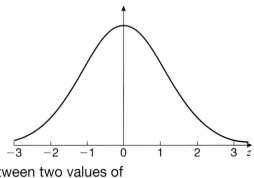

The total area under the Normal curve is 1. The area between two values of z gives the probability that the random variable lies between those values.

Using Normal probability tables to find probabilities

The Normal probability tables you will get in the examination are for a mean of 0 and a standard deviation of 1. To use the tables you need to **standardise** the Normal distribution you are working with. You do this by subtracting the mean and then dividing by the standard deviation.

$$z = \frac{x - \mu}{\sigma}$$

EXAMPLE 1

Adult men in the UK have a mean height of 175 cm. The standard deviation is 7.5 cm. You can assume that the heights are Normally distributed. Find the probability that a randomly chosen man is shorter than 180 cm.

SOLUTION

What you need to write down	What is happening
H = height of a randomly chosen adult man in cm.	Say what the letters you introduce stand for.
$P(H < 180)$	This is the probability you were asked to find.
$P\left(\dfrac{H - 175}{7.5} < \dfrac{180 - 175}{7.5}\right)$	Standardise by subtracting the mean and dividing by the standard deviation.
$P(Z < 0.667)$	$\dfrac{H - 175}{7.5}$ is now the standard Normal random variable. It is given the symbol Z.
The probability is 0.7477. The probability of a randomly chosen man being shorter than 180 cm is 0.748 (to 3 d.p.).	Use Normal probability tables (see below) then round probability to 3 d.p. Write down what you have found the probability of and check that this is what the question asked you to find.

Standard Normal with mean 0 and standard deviation 1
$P(Z < 0.667)$ is 0.748 (3 d.p.)

(add)

z	.06	5	6	7
0.6	7454		19	23
0.7	7764		18	21

3rd decimal place

$7454 + 23 = 7477$

The probability is the shaded area under the standard Normal curve.

⚠️ On some graphical calculators you can type in the mean, standard deviation and the values that you want the Normal random variable to lie between and get the probability displayed on screen. This is very useful for checking. However, if you type in the wrong number you will get the wrong answer. You cannot get any marks if you just write down an answer and it is wrong. Showing your working by standardising will get you some marks even if your final answer is wrong.

EXAMPLE 2

Adult men in the UK have a mean height of 175 cm. The standard deviation is 7.5 cm. You can assume that the heights are Normally distributed. Find the probability that a randomly chosen man is taller than 180 cm.

SOLUTION

This is the same distribution as in Example 1. You are asked to find $P(H > 180)$. You worked out $P(H < 180) = 0.7477$ in Example 1.
$P(H > 180) = 1 - P(H < 180) = 1 - 0.7477 = 0.2523$
The probability that a randomly chosen man is taller than 180 cm is 0.252 (to 3 d.p.).

A ADVICE

You may remember that for the Poisson and binomial distributions, it makes a difference whether you are working out $P(X > 3)$ or $P(X \geqslant 3)$. This is because they are discrete distributions and the probabilities for these ranges are found by adding up individual probabilities so whether $P(X = 3)$ is included makes a difference. The Normal distribution is continuous and the total probability is given by the area under the curve. Whether the line at $X = 3$ is included or not, it makes no difference to the area. So, for Example 2 above, $P(H > 180)$ is the same as $P(H \geqslant 180)$.

EXAMPLE 3

Every day, Anita goes for a walk. She always takes the same route and she finds that the time she takes is Normally distributed with mean 28.5 minutes and standard deviation 1.7 minutes. What is the probability that her walk takes between 25 and 30 minutes?

SOLUTION

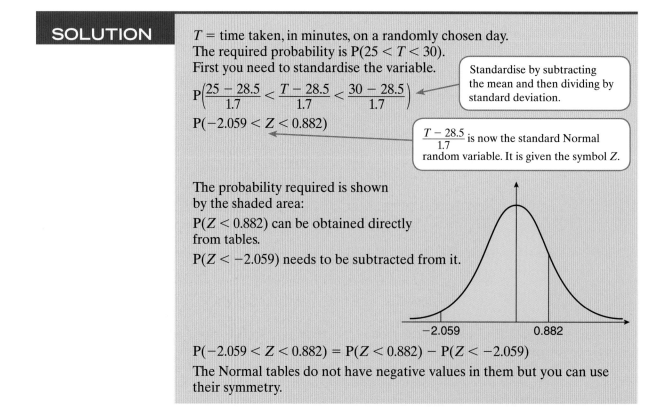

T = time taken, in minutes, on a randomly chosen day.
The required probability is $P(25 < T < 30)$.
First you need to standardise the variable.

> Standardise by subtracting the mean and then dividing by standard deviation.

$$P\left(\frac{25 - 28.5}{1.7} < \frac{T - 28.5}{1.7} < \frac{30 - 28.5}{1.7}\right)$$
$$P(-2.059 < Z < 0.882)$$

> $\frac{T - 28.5}{1.7}$ is now the standard Normal random variable. It is given the symbol Z.

The probability required is shown by the shaded area:
$P(Z < 0.882)$ can be obtained directly from tables.
$P(Z < -2.059)$ needs to be subtracted from it.

$P(-2.059 < Z < 0.882) = P(Z < 0.882) - P(Z < -2.059)$
The Normal tables do not have negative values in them but you can use their symmetry.

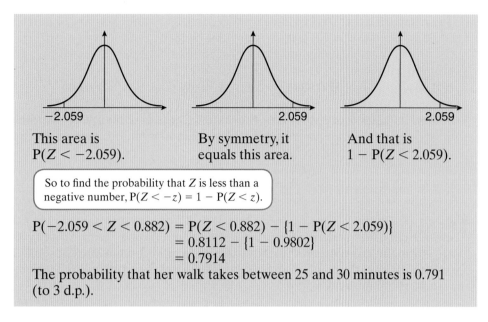

-2.059 ... 2.059 ... 2.059

This area is
P(Z < −2.059).

By symmetry, it
equals this area.

And that is
1 − P(Z < 2.059).

So to find the probability that Z is less than a
negative number, P(Z < −z) = 1 − P(Z < z).

$$P(-2.059 < Z < 0.882) = P(Z < 0.882) - \{1 - P(Z < 2.059)\}$$
$$= 0.8112 - \{1 - 0.9802\}$$
$$= 0.7914$$

The probability that her walk takes between 25 and 30 minutes is 0.791
(to 3 d.p.).

A ADVICE

When you are working with Normal probabilities, draw a sketch of the standard Normal
distribution curve and shade the area that you are trying to find. This will help you get the right
answer.

You need to divide by the standard deviation when standardising. If you are told the variance, you
will need to find the square root of it first. If you know that $X \sim N(3, 1.44)$, this means that X has a
mean of 3 and a variance of 1.44. The standard deviation is 1.2.

LINKS

Statistics   Continuous Random Variables (S3); Central Limit
Theorem (S3).

Test Yourself ▷L

1 $X \sim N(5, 16)$. This means that X has a Normal distribution. Which one of the following statements
is true?
A The mean is 4 and the standard deviation is 5
B The mean is 5 and the standard deviation is 4
C The mean is 5 and the standard deviation is 16
D The mean is 16 and the standard deviation is 5
E The mean is 16 and the standard deviation is 2.24 (3 s.f.)

2 A bakery produces loaves of bread with mean weight 400 g. The weights of loaves are Normally
distributed with standard deviation 10 g. What is the probability that a randomly selected loaf
weighs less than 395 g? (Answers are given to 3 d.p.)
A 0.309   B 0.500   C 0.692   D 0.832
E It is not possible to work it out because the standardised value is negative.

3 The mean time that it takes the eggs of a particular variety of bird to hatch is 23.5 days. The standard deviation is 1.2 days. Assume that hatching times follow a Normal distribution. What is the probability that a randomly chosen egg takes between 21 and 24 days to hatch? (Answers are given to 3 d.p.)

A 0.034   B 0.320   C 0.595   D 0.643   E 0.644

4 A machine dispenses cups of tea. The volumes of tea are Normally distributed with a standard deviation 1.4 ml. What proportion of cups of tea contain a volume of tea that is within 2 ml of the mean? (Answers given to 3 s.f.)

A 11.4%   B 42.4%   C 84.7%   D 92.4%

E It is impossible to work out without knowing what the mean is.

5 Adult men in the UK have a mean height of 175 cm. Adult women in the UK have a mean height of 161.6 cm. The standard deviation for each population is 7.5 cm. You can assume that the heights are Normally distributed. An adult man and an adult woman are chosen at random. What is the probability that the man is shorter than 170 cm but the woman is taller than 170 cm? (Answers are given to 3 d.p.)

A 0.033   B 0.205   C 0.384   D 0.649   E 0.683

Exam-Style Question

A survey shows that the systolic blood pressure of women in the UK is Normally distributed with mean 121 mm Hg and standard deviation 16.2 mm Hg.

i) Hypertension is defined as a systolic blood pressure over 140 mm Hg. What proportion of women in the UK suffer from hypertension?

ii) Ten women are chosen at random from the population. Find the probability that at least one of them has hypertension.

Using inverse Normal probability tables

A ABOUT THIS TOPIC

In the last section you used standard Normal tables to find the probability that a Normal variable lies in a particular range. Sometimes you will want to know high (or low) values of the variable that together have a particular probability. You will use this idea in hypothesis testing and you will have inverse Normal tables provided in the examination to help you.

R REMEMBER

- How to solve equations and simultaneous equations from GCSE.
- If a random variable, X, has a Normal distribution with mean μ and standard deviation σ, this can be written as $X \sim N(\mu, \sigma^2)$.

K KEY FACTS

- Standard Normal tables are for a Normal distribution with mean 0 and standard deviation 1. A variable with this distribution is often given the symbol Z. $Z \sim N(0, 1)$.

- Standard Normal tables give the probability that Z is less than a particular value (z). This is represented by the shaded area in the diagram.

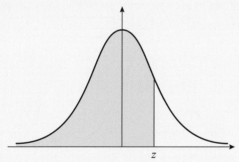

- The total area under the Normal curve is 1.

- To use standard Normal tables, other Normal variables have to be standardised by subtracting the mean and then dividing by the standard deviation. $z = \dfrac{x - \mu}{\sigma}$.

- Inverse Normal tables give the value of z which matches up with the probability of being less than that value.

What do the inverse Normal probability tables do?

Both the Normal tables and the inverse Normal tables are for the standard Normal distribution with mean 0 and standard deviation 1.

Both tables deal with the relationship between a given value, z, and the probability, p, that the standard Normal variable is less than it.

The Normal tables tell you p if you know z.

The inverse Normal tables tell you z if you know p.

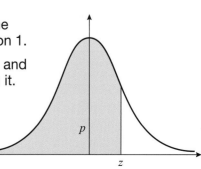

EXAMPLE 1

Adult men in the UK have a mean height of 175 cm. The standard deviation is 7.5 cm. You can assume that the heights are Normally distributed.

i) Find the upper quartile.

ii) Find the lower quartile.

SOLUTION

H = height of a randomly chosen adult man in cm.

$H \sim N(175, 7.5^2)$ ◄─── Summarise the information in the question.

i) The probability of a man being shorter than the upper quartile is 0.75.

$P(H < h) = 0.75$, where h is the upper quartile.

To standardise, subtract the mean and divide by the standard deviation.

$$\frac{h - 175}{7.5} = z$$

Notice that lower case h and z are used as this question is about particular values of the random variables.

Use inverse Normal tables to look up the value of z such that $P(Z < z) = 0.75$.

p	.000
.75	.6745

0.75

$z = 0.6745$

$$\frac{h - 175}{7.5} = 0.6745$$

You found that $z = 0.6745$ from tables. Now multiply each side by 7.5.

$h - 175 = 5.058\ldots$

$h = 175 + 5.058\ldots = 180.05\ldots$

$h \approx 180.1$

One or two decimal places is enough to give for height.

The upper quartile is 180.1 cm.

ii) The probability of a man being shorter than the lower quartile is 0.25.

0.25

The inverse Normal tables do not have values of p less than 0.5.

You can see from the diagram that the value of z is less than zero. By symmetry, it is the negative of the value you found in part **i)**.

$z = -0.6745$

$$\frac{h - 175}{7.5} = -0.6745$$

$h - 175 = -5.058\ldots$

$h = 169.94\ldots$

$h \approx 169.9$

The working is very similar to part **i)**.

The lower quartile is 169.9 cm.

A ADVICE

Always draw a sketch of the standard Normal curve. Remember that the line of symmetry is at $z = 0$ and the area each side of the line of symmetry is 0.5. Shading the probability you have as an area will help you get the right value of z.

Finding mean and/or standard deviation from probability

Sometimes you will know that data are Normally distributed but not know the mean and standard deviation. If you know the probability of data values being in a particular range you can work out mean or standard deviation or both.

EXAMPLE 2

Heights of adult men in China are Normally distributed. 12.7% of men are shorter than 160 cm and 21.2% of men are taller than 174 cm. Find the mean and standard deviation of the heights of adult men in China.

SOLUTION

M stands for the height, in cm, of a randomly chosen Chinese man. The population mean is μ cm and the standard deviation is σ cm.

$M \sim N(\mu, \sigma^2)$

12.7% of men are shorter than 160 cm.
$P(M < 160) = 0.127$

Standardising, $P\left(Z < \dfrac{160 - \mu}{\sigma}\right) = 0.127.$

> Remember to say what the letters you introduce stand for.

The diagram shows you that the standardised value, z_1 is negative because it is to the left of the mean so use symmetry to get the equivalent positive value (call this $z_1{}'$).

By symmetry, the area to the left of the positive value is $1 - 0.127 = 0.873$.
Using inverse Normal tables:

$z_1{}' = 1.141$
$z_1 = -1.141$

p	.003
.87	1.141

> 3rd decimal place

This standardised value was also equal to $\dfrac{160 - \mu}{\sigma}$

so

$$\dfrac{160 - \mu}{\sigma} = -1.141$$

$$160 - \mu = -1.141\sigma \qquad \textbf{(1)}$$

> Multiplying each side by σ.

This gives one equation connecting μ and σ.

Looking at the other inequality will give you another equation.

21.2% of men are taller than 174 cm.
$P(M > 174) = 0.212$

Standardising, $P\left(Z > \dfrac{174 - \mu}{\sigma}\right) = 0.212.$

$$P(Z > z_2) = 0.212$$
$$P(Z < z_2) = 1 - 0.212$$
$$\qquad\qquad = 0.788$$
$$z_2 = 0.7995$$

p	.008
.78	.7995

> Remember the tables only give probabilities of being less than a value.

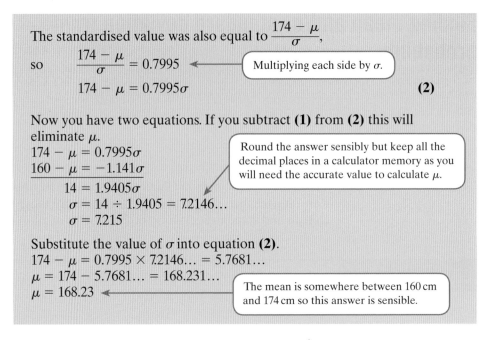

The standardised value was also equal to $\dfrac{174 - \mu}{\sigma}$,

so $\dfrac{174 - \mu}{\sigma} = 0.7995$ ◀— Multiplying each side by σ.

$$174 - \mu = 0.7995\sigma \qquad \textbf{(2)}$$

Now you have two equations. If you subtract **(1)** from **(2)** this will eliminate μ.

Round the answer sensibly but keep all the decimal places in a calculator memory as you will need the accurate value to calculate μ.

$$174 - \mu = 0.7995\sigma$$
$$\underline{160 - \mu = -1.141\sigma}$$
$$14 = 1.9405\sigma$$
$$\sigma = 14 \div 1.9405 = 7.2146\ldots$$
$$\sigma = 7.215$$

Substitute the value of σ into equation **(2)**.
$$174 - \mu = 0.7995 \times 7.2146\ldots = 5.7681\ldots$$
$$\mu = 174 - 5.7681\ldots = 168.231\ldots$$
$$\mu = 168.23$$ ◀—

The mean is somewhere between 160 cm and 174 cm so this answer is sensible.

A ADVICE

There are a lot of stages to this kind of question. Be careful to show working clearly and think about whether the answers you are getting are sensible.

LINKS

Statistics   Hypothesis Tests using the Normal Distribution (S2);
              Confidence Intervals using the Normal Distribution (S3).

Test Yourself ▷L

This information is for questions 1 and 2.

A particular variety of sunflower grows to a mean height of 185 cm. The standard deviation is 17 cm. The heights of sunflower plants are Normally distributed.

1 For this variety of sunflower plants, 10% are above a particular height. What is this height? (Answers are in cm to 1 d.p.)

   A 128.2   B 163.2   C 203.3   D 206.8   E 555.5

2 For this variety of sunflower plants, 5% are below a particular height. What is this height? (Answers are in cm to 1 d.p.)

   A 157.0   B 157.8   C 185.9   D 213.0

   E You can't do it because the tables don't go below 0.5.

3 A machine makes bolts which should be 5 cm long. 15% of the bolts produced are shorter than 4.75 cm. The manager thinks that the machine is faulty and that the mean is different from 5 cm. The lengths of bolts produced are Normally distributed with standard deviation 0.07 cm. What is the mean? (Answers are in cm to 3 d.p.)

   A 4.677   B 4.753   C 4.755   D 4.806   E 4.823

4 Sixth form students living in a particular area carry school bags which have a mean weight of 6.3 kg. The weights of the bags are Normally distributed. 14.6% of students carry bags which weigh over 8 kg. What is the standard deviation of the weights of the bags? (Answers are in kg to 3 d.p.)

A 0.646   B 1.270   C 1.613   D 2.601   E 11.644

5 19% of a population of men have feet that are over 29 cm long. 8% of the same population have feet that are shorter than 25 cm. Foot length is Normally distributed. Find the mean and standard deviation. (Answers are in cm to 1 d.p.)

A $\mu = 8.2\ \sigma = 23.7$ B $\mu = 35.7\ \sigma = -7.6$ C $\mu = 22.1\ \sigma = 36.4$ D $\mu = 27.5\ \sigma = 1.8$

Exam-Style Question ⋑L

The time that it takes an experienced fruit picker to pick a basket of strawberries is Normally distributed with mean 12 minutes and standard deviation 1.5 minutes. A basket of fruit is chosen at random. What is the probability that the time taken to pick this basket was

i) greater than 15 minutes?

ii) less than 10 minutes?

A new fruit picker starts work. 8% of the baskets of strawberries she picks take her longer than 15 minutes. 5% of them take less than 10 minutes.

iii) Assuming that the time the new picker takes to pick a basket of strawberries is also Normally distributed, find the mean and standard deviation for her.

Modelling using a Normal distribution

One of the first uses of the Normal distribution was to analyse errors in measurement. Most errors are small; larger errors are less common. If the sign of the error is taken into account, the bell-shaped curve of the Normal distribution provides a good fit to the distribution of errors. Many naturally occurring variables are, at least approximately, Normally distributed.

- Rounding and limits of accuracy from GCSE.
- Standard Normal tables are for a Normal distribution with mean 0 and standard deviation 1. A variable with this distribution is often given the symbol Z. $Z \sim N(0, 1)$.
- Using standard Normal tables from previous sections.

K KEY FACTS

- The Normal curve is symmetrical so any distribution which shows noticeable skew cannot be modelled by a Normal distribution.

- The peak of the Normal curve is at the mean. Distributions with different means but the same standard deviation will be translations of each other.

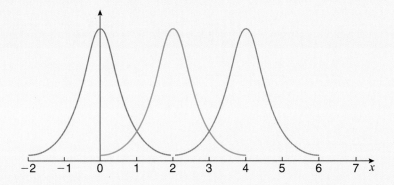

- For two distributions with the same mean but different standard deviations, the one with the larger standard deviation has a wider curve; the curve is also lower so that the total area under it is still 1.

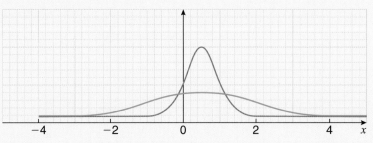

- The Normal distribution is for a continuous variable. If it is used as an approximating distribution for a discrete variable, a continuity correction must be used. For example, values from 12.5 up to 13.5 for the approximating Normal would correspond to a value of 13 for the discrete variable.

When is the Normal distribution used?

The diastolic blood pressures of a sample of 100 adults are shown in the histogram. The Normal distribution curve on the diagram has the same mean and standard deviation. It seems reasonable to assume that the Normal curve would be a reasonably good match for the blood pressures of the whole adult population.

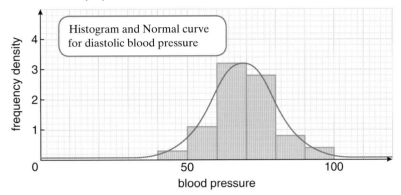

Histogram and Normal curve for diastolic blood pressure

A ADVICE

Examination questions will often tell you when to use a Normal distribution but users of statistics sometimes have to decide for themselves whether a Normal distribution is appropriate. You will learn about some situations where a Normal approximation can be used in the next two sections.

EXAMPLE 1

The histogram shows the distribution of weights of patients in a hospital. Explain why the Normal distribution would not be appropriate for this population.

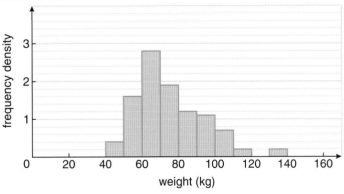

SOLUTION

The distribution of weights is positively skewed but the Normal distribution is symmetrical so it cannot be used as a model for this distribution of weights.

Modelling discrete situations

IQ tests give a whole number score. They are designed to follow a Normal distribution with the mean for the whole population being 100 and the population standard deviation 15. The distribution of scores is shown in the vertical line chart.

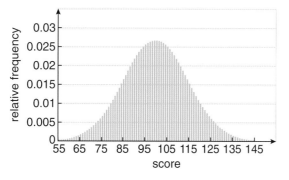

The scores which candidates receive can only be integers so the score is a discrete variable but the Normal distribution is for a continuous variable. To use the Normal distribution for a discrete variable, a **continuity correction** has to be used. An example of this is given below.

EXAMPLE 2

An IQ test is designed so that the scores follow a Normal distribution with a mean of 100 and a standard deviation of 15. Candidates can only get integer scores. Find the proportion of people taking the test who score between 110 and 115 marks (inclusive).

SOLUTION

It will help you to think of the integer score (X) which candidates get and the 'unrounded' score (S), which is Normally distributed.

Scores from 110 to 115 correspond to unrounded values from 109.5 up to 115.5.

$P(110 \leqslant X \leqslant 115)$ corresponds to $P(109.5 \leqslant S < 115.5)$.

S 109.5   115.5

X 109   110   111   112   113   114   115   116

> 109.5 is the lowest number which rounds to 110. At the upper end of the range, numbers up to 115.5 will round to 115.

$S \sim N(100, 15^2)$

> It is the 'unrounded' score which is Normally distributed with mean 100 and standard deviation 15.

Standardising $P(109.5 \leqslant S < 115.5) = P\left(\dfrac{109.5 - 100}{15} \leqslant Z < \dfrac{115.5 - 100}{15}\right)$

$P(0.633 \leqslant Z < 1.033) = P(Z \leqslant 1.033) - P(Z \leqslant 0.633)$

> Subtract the mean (100) and divide by the standard deviation (15).

> From the Normal curve diagram. Remember it does not make a difference to the answer whether you use $<$ or $\leqslant$ for a Normal random variable.

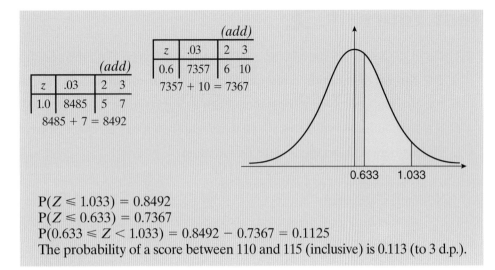

$P(Z \leqslant 1.033) = 0.8492$
$P(Z \leqslant 0.633) = 0.7367$
$P(0.633 \leqslant Z < 1.033) = 0.8492 - 0.7367 = 0.1125$
The probability of a score between 110 and 115 (inclusive) is 0.113 (to 3 d.p.).

A ADVICE

You will need continuity corrections when working with Normal approximations to binomial and Poisson distributions; these are covered in the next two sections. You will find it easiest if you think what 'unrounded' values would match to the integer values you need. Some examples are given in the table below. Try to cover up the second row and work out what it should say.

Examples of continuity corrections

Discrete variable, X	$X > 100$	$X \geqslant 100$	$X < 105$	$X \leqslant 105$
Approximating Normal, S	$S \geqslant 100.5$	$S \geqslant 99.5$	$S < 104.5$	$S < 105.5$

 For the Normal distribution, it does not make a difference whether the inequality sign includes equals but it does make a difference for a discrete distribution.

 LINKS

Statistics   Normal approximation to the Binomial and Poisson Distributions (S2); χ^2 Test for Goodness of Fit (S3).

Test Yourself

1 Three of the following statements are false and one is true. Find the one that is true.

   A The Normal distribution cannot be used as an approximation to a discrete variable.

   B If a distribution is symmetrical then it can be approximated by a Normal distribution.

   C If a distribution is symmetrical and unimodal then it has an exact Normal distribution.

   D The histogram shows the lengths of a random sample of 15 pea pods. The lengths of the whole population of pea pods could be Normally distributed.

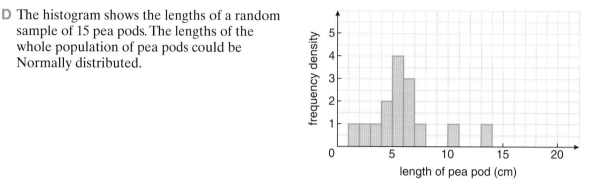

2 X is a discrete random variable which can only take integer values. X is approximately Normal. Y is the Normal distribution with the same mean and variance as X. Which Normal probability best approximates $P(X > 8)$?

   A $P(Y > 7.5)$ B $P(Y \geqslant 8)$ C $P(Y > 8)$ D $P(Y \geqslant 8.5)$ E $P(Y \geqslant 9.5)$

3 X is a discrete random variable which can only take integer values. X is approximately Normal. Y is the Normal distribution with the same mean and variance as X. Which Normal probability best approximates $P(1 < X < 6)$?

   A $P(0.5 \leqslant Y \leqslant 5.5)$ B $P(0.5 \leqslant Y \leqslant 6.5)$ C $P(1 \leqslant Y \leqslant 6)$

   D $P(1.5 \leqslant Y < 5.5)$ E $P(1.5 \leqslant Y < 6.5)$

4 Marks awarded in a test can only be integers. The distribution of marks is approximately Normal with mean 45.4 and standard deviation 16. A mark of 70 or over is awarded a distinction. What proportion of candidates for the test is awarded a distinction? (Answers are given to 1 d.p.)

   A 5.8%   B 6.2%   C 6.6%   D 46.3%   E 93.4%

Exam-Style Question

A random sample of 180 students is asked to complete a puzzle. The times taken are shown in the table.

Time x minutes	$0 < x \leqslant 2$	$2 < x \leqslant 3$	$3 < x \leqslant 4$	$4 < x \leqslant 5$	$5 < x \leqslant 8$
Frequency	2	52	82	27	17

i) Estimate the mean and standard deviation of these data.

ii) If times taken to complete the puzzle are Normally distributed, with mean and standard deviation the values you found in part i), how many students out of 180 would you expect to take between 4 and 5 minutes?

iii) Do you think that the Normal distribution is a good model for these data? Give a reason for your answer.

Normal approximation to the binomial distribution

A ABOUT THIS TOPIC

The first use of the Normal distribution was as an approximation to the binomial distribution. In the eighteenth century, mathematician Abraham de Moivre worked out odds for gamblers in the coffee houses. He found that, when n was large, he could use a Normal approximation to work out binomial probabilities more quickly.

R REMEMBER

- The binomial distribution from S1.
- Using standard Normal tables and inverse Normal tables from previous sections.
- The Normal distribution is for a continuous variable. If it is used as an approximating distribution for a binomial variable, a continuity correction must be used. For example, values from 12.5 up to 13.5 for the approximating Normal would correspond to a value of 13 for the binomial variable.

K KEY FACTS

- The expectation of a binomial random variable is $E(X) = np$.
- The variance of a binomial random variable is $Var(X) = npq$, where $q = 1 - p$.
- The binomial distribution with parameters n and p can be approximated by a Normal distribution with mean np and variance npq as long as n is large and p is not too close to 0 or 1.

When can the Normal distribution be used as an approximation to the binomial distribution?

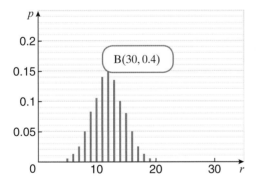

A ADVICE

You do not need to memorise any rules of thumb to help you decide whether a Normal approximation to the binomial is appropriate. It will be clear from examination questions whether you can use it in the S2 examination and you will be able to look up such rules if you think you may need to use an approximation when making practical calculations.

When n is large and p is not too far from 0.5, the Normal approximation gives reasonably accurate values for binomial probabilities and it allows them to be calculated more easily.

There are several rules of thumb in use to decide whether n is large enough, and p near enough 0.5, for the Normal approximation to be used. One such rule says that np and $n(1 - p)$ should both be over 5. The larger n is, the further p can be from 0.5.

- The expectation of a binomial random variable is $E(X) = np$.
- The variance of a binomial random variable is $Var(X) = npq$, where $q = 1 - p$.
- The binomial distribution $B(n, p)$ can be approximated by the Normal distribution $N(np, npq)$ as long as n is large and p is not too close to 0 or 1. A continuity correction is needed.

Using the formula Var $(X) = npq$ will tell you the variance of the approximating Normal distribution. Remember that when you standardise the Normal you need to divide by the standard deviation. You will need to find the square root of the variance to get the standard deviation.

EXAMPLE 1

Euro coins have different designs in different European countries. In 2002, an experiment with Belgian 1 euro coins resulted in 140 heads in 250 spins. Use a suitable approximating distribution to find the probability that a fair coin will land heads at least 140 times in 250 trials.

SOLUTION

X = the number of heads in 250 trials of a fair coin.

> Remember that for a binomial distribution you are repeating the same experiment n times with a fixed probability of success, p, each time.

X has a binomial distribution with $n = 250$ and $p = 0.5$.

Mean $= np = 250 \times 0.5 = 125$

Variance $= npq = 250 \times 0.5 \times 0.5 = 62.5$

> $q = 1 - p = 1 - 0.5 = 0.5$

X is approximately Normal, $N(125, 62.5)$.

$P(X \geq 140)$ is required but a continuity correction is needed; this gives $P(X \geq 139.5)$

> 139.5
> 140 141 142 143
> Think what numbers would round to 140 or over.

Standardise (subtract the mean and divide by the standard deviation)

$$P\left(Z \geq \frac{139.5 - 125}{\sqrt{62.5}}\right)$$

> 62.5 is the variance but you need to divide by the standard deviation.

$P(Z \geq 1.834) = 1 - P(Z \leq 1.834)$

$P(Z \geq 1.834) = 1 - 0.9667$

$P(Z \geq 1.834) = 0.0333$

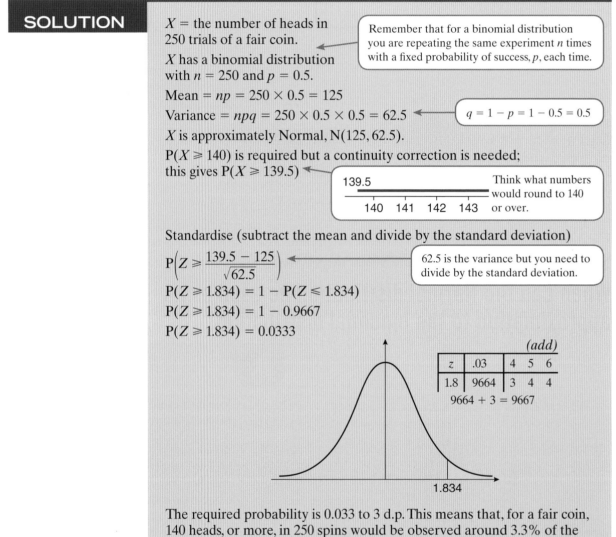

			(add)		
z	.03		4	5	6
1.8	9664		3	4	4

$9664 + 3 = 9667$

1.834

The required probability is 0.033 to 3 d.p. This means that, for a fair coin, 140 heads, or more, in 250 spins would be observed around 3.3% of the time.

A ADVICE

Computers or graphical calculators can find exact binomial probabilities for large values of n. However, if you are asked to use an approximate method in an examination then you must do so. If you have time and a graphical calculator that will give the exact value then you can use this to check your answer. The exact binomial probability for Example 1 is 0.0332 (to 4 d.p.) and this agrees well with the approximate Normal answer that was found above.

Which approximation to use for a binomial distribution?

You know two approximations to the binomial distribution: the Poisson distribution and the Normal distribution. Questions may tell you to use an approximate distribution for a binomial distribution but you will need to decide which is appropriate.

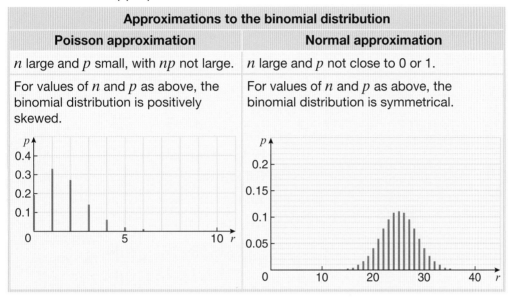

Approximations to the binomial distribution	
Poisson approximation	**Normal approximation**
n large and p small, with np not large.	n large and p not close to 0 or 1.
For values of n and p as above, the binomial distribution is positively skewed.	For values of n and p as above, the binomial distribution is symmetrical.

For very large values of n, the Normal approximation is good even for fairly small or fairly large values of p. If n is large, np is over 5 and $n(1 - p)$ is also over 5 then you can probably use the Normal approximation.

Calculating a value from a probability

EXAMPLE 2

A restaurant has taken a booking for a party of 40 guests. Each woman in the group will be given a rose. Assume that each person in the group has an equal probability of being male or female (from the restaurant's point of view). How many roses does the restaurant need to be 95% sure of not running out. (Use a Normal approximation.)

SOLUTION

For each person, the probability of needing a rose is 0.5 and there are 40 people so the number of roses needed has a binomial distribution with $n = 40$ and $p = 0.5$.

X = number of roses needed.

Mean = np = 40 × 0.5 = 20

Variance = npq = 40 × 0.5 × 0.5 = 10 ← $q = 1 - p = 1 - 0.5 = 0.5$

X is approximately Normal, N(20, 10).

You need to find the number x such that $P(X \leqslant x) = 0.95$ but a continuity correction is needed so

$P(X < x + 0.5) = 0.95$

Remember x is a whole number. Whatever number it is, values up to $x + 0.5$ will round to x or fewer.

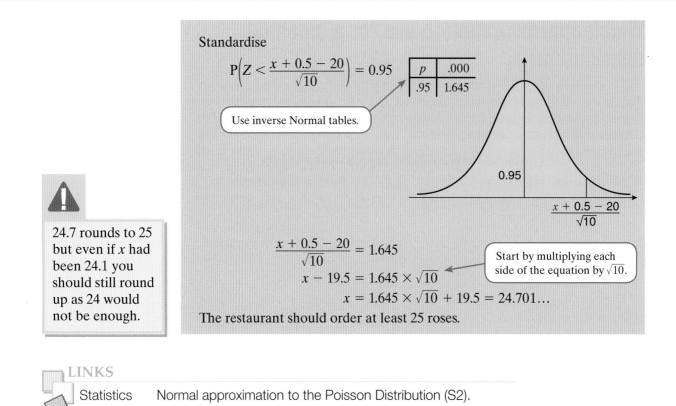

Standardise

$$P\left(Z < \frac{x + 0.5 - 20}{\sqrt{10}}\right) = 0.95$$

p	.000
.95	1.645

Use inverse Normal tables.

0.95

$$\frac{x + 0.5 - 20}{\sqrt{10}}$$

24.7 rounds to 25 but even if x had been 24.1 you should still round up as 24 would not be enough.

$$\frac{x + 0.5 - 20}{\sqrt{10}} = 1.645$$
$$x - 19.5 = 1.645 \times \sqrt{10}$$
$$x = 1.645 \times \sqrt{10} + 19.5 = 24.701\ldots$$

Start by multiplying each side of the equation by $\sqrt{10}$.

The restaurant should order at least 25 roses.

LINKS

Statistics   Normal approximation to the Poisson Distribution (S2).

Test Yourself ▷L

1 A computer based 'psychic test' asks the user to guess which of 5 shapes the computer will display next. Users have 100 goes at guessing the shape. Each shape is equally likely to come up. What is the mean and standard deviation of the number of correct guesses? (You should assume that the users are just guessing and do not have psychic powers.)

A Mean = 100, standard deviation = 0.2   B Mean = 100, standard deviation = 5

C Mean = 20, standard deviation = 16   D Mean = 20, standard deviation ≈ 4.47

E Mean = 20, standard deviation = 4

2 Three per cent of the children in a region have food allergies. A school in this region allocates students to classes independently and at random. Each class has 30 students. What approximating distribution could be used for the number of students in a class with food allergies?

A B(30, 0.03)   B N(30, 0.03)   C N(0.9, 0.873)   D Poisson(0.9)   E Poisson(0.934)

3 Students take a 40-question test. For each question they have to say whether a statement is true or false. Use an approximating distribution to find the probability that a student who guesses every answer will get at least 25 questions right. Give your answer to 3 decimal places.

A 0.057   B 0.077   C 0.157   D 0.326

4 Fruit jelly sweets are packed in boxes containing 35 sweets; 25% of fruit jelly sweets produced are raspberry flavoured. All flavours are well mixed before packing. Use a suitable approximating distribution to find the probability that a box of fruit jelly sweets contains fewer than 5 raspberry flavoured ones. Give your answer to 3 decimal places.

A 0.049   B 0.064   C 0.072   D 0.259

5 A revision guide contains 100 multiple choice questions. There are 5 answers to choose from for each question. Use an approximating distribution to find a number, x, such that a student who guesses on every question has a smaller than 1% chance of getting x, or more, questions right.

A 25   B 27   C 29   D 30   E 58

Exam-Style Question ⊃L

A restaurant has a choice of desserts on the menu. Past experience shows that 30% of customers choose apple pie. The restaurant serves 60 diners in a typical evening.

Assume that a binomial distribution provides a suitable model for the number of customers out of a sample of 60 who choose apple pie.

i) How many customers out of the sample of 60 would be expected to choose apple pie?

ii) Using a suitable approximating distribution, find the probability that more than 20 customers choose apple pie.

iii) How many portions of apple pie need to be available for the restaurant manager to be 99% sure that they will not run out of apple pie?

Normal approximation to the Poisson distribution

A ABOUT THIS TOPIC

For small values of the mean, λ, the Poisson(λ) distribution is positively skewed so the Normal distribution cannot be used as an approximation to it. For large values of λ, the Poisson distribution is much more symmetrical and the Normal distribution can be used as an approximation to it.

R REMEMBER

- The Poisson distribution from previous sections.
- Using standard Normal tables and inverse Normal tables from previous sections.
- The Normal distribution is for a continuous variable. If it is used as an approximating distribution for a Poisson variable, a continuity correction must be used. For example, values from 2.5 up to 3.5 for the approximating Normal would correspond to a value of 3 for the Poisson variable.

K KEY FACTS

- The expectation and variance of the Poisson(λ) distribution are each λ.
- The Poisson(λ) distribution can be approximated by a Normal distribution with mean λ and variance λ as long as λ is large enough. (If λ is 10, or more, that is usually large enough.)

When can the Normal distribution be used as an approximation to the Poisson distribution?

When the Poisson distribution has a large mean, the Normal approximation gives reasonably accurate values for the probabilities and it allows them to be calculated more easily.

One rule of thumb which is sometimes used in deciding whether a Normal approximation can be used for a Poisson distribution is to say that λ should be 10, or more.

A ADVICE

It is not possible to give a rule to say exactly when the Normal approximation to the Poisson can be used. It depends partly on how accurately probabilities are needed and also on whether it is possible to calculate exact Poisson probabilities easily, using a suitable calculator or computer. In S2 exam questions, it will be clear when you should use a Normal approximation to the Poisson.
- The expectation (i.e. the mean) and the variance of the Poisson(λ) distribution are each λ.
- The Poisson(λ) distribution can be approximated by a Normal distribution with mean λ and variance λ as long as λ is large enough.

EXAMPLE 1

The number of new cases of a rare and non-infectious illness in a region can be modelled using a Poisson distribution. The number of new cases per year has a mean of 38.2. Health service managers are planning how much money to put into the budget for treating the illness. Use a suitable approximating distribution to find that probability that there will be more than 45 cases of the illness in the coming year

SOLUTION

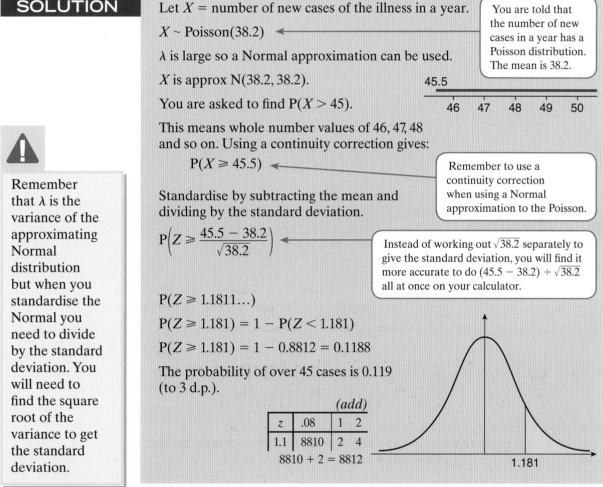

Let X = number of new cases of the illness in a year.

$X \sim \text{Poisson}(38.2)$

You are told that the number of new cases in a year has a Poisson distribution. The mean is 38.2.

λ is large so a Normal approximation can be used.

X is approx $N(38.2, 38.2)$.

You are asked to find $P(X > 45)$.

This means whole number values of 46, 47, 48 and so on. Using a continuity correction gives:

$P(X \geqslant 45.5)$

Remember to use a continuity correction when using a Normal approximation to the Poisson.

Standardise by subtracting the mean and dividing by the standard deviation.

$P\left(Z \geqslant \dfrac{45.5 - 38.2}{\sqrt{38.2}}\right)$

Instead of working out $\sqrt{38.2}$ separately to give the standard deviation, you will find it more accurate to do $(45.5 - 38.2) \div \sqrt{38.2}$ all at once on your calculator.

$P(Z \geqslant 1.1811\ldots)$

$P(Z \geqslant 1.181) = 1 - P(Z < 1.181)$

$P(Z \geqslant 1.181) = 1 - 0.8812 = 0.1188$

The probability of over 45 cases is 0.119 (to 3 d.p.).

z	.08	1	2
1.1	8810	2	4

(add)

$8810 + 2 = 8812$

Remember that λ is the variance of the approximating Normal distribution but when you standardise the Normal you need to divide by the standard deviation. You will need to find the square root of the variance to get the standard deviation.

A | ADVICE

You could not use Poisson tables to do Example 1 because they only go up to $\lambda = 10.9$. Computers or graphical calculators can find exact Poisson probabilities. However, if you are asked to use an approximate method in an examination then you must do so. If you have time and a graphical calculator that will give the exact value then you can use this to check your answer. The exact probability for Example 1 is 0.1205 (to 4 d.p.) and this agrees well with the approximate Normal answer that was found above

---

EXAMPLE 2

Could you use an approximate Normal distribution to find the probability that there will be more than 4 cases in a month? Give a reason for your answer.

SOLUTION

The mean number of cases in a month will be $38.2 \div 12 = 3.1833\ldots$. The number of cases in a month will have a Poisson distribution but the mean is not big so the Normal approximation should not be used.

 If you have used a Poisson distribution to approximate a binomial distribution, you should not approximate this Poisson again with a Normal distribution. Remember you should only use the Poisson approximation to the binomial when the mean, np, is not too big but you can only use the Normal approximation to the Poisson when the mean is big.

EXAMPLE 3

A stall at a fundraising coffee morning offers a prize for guessing the exact number of chocolate chips in a chocolate chip cookie. Each of the numbers from 5 to 30 (inclusive) is guessed by at least one person. There are no guesses for fewer than 5 or more than 30. The number of chocolate chips in a randomly selected cookie has a Poisson distribution with mean 24. What is the probability that no-one has guessed correctly?

SOLUTION

Let X = the number of chocolate chips in a randomly selected cookie.
$X \sim \text{Poisson}(24)$.
P(no-one has guessed correctly) = $P(X < 5) + P(X > 30)$
$X \sim N(24, 24)$ approx

> X is less than 5 or more than 30 if no-one has guessed correctly.

Continuity corrections:

P(no-one has guessed correctly) = $P(X < 4.5) + P(X \geqslant 30.5)$

> The numbers which round to less than 5 are less than 4.5.
>
> The numbers which round to more than 30 are 30.5 and over.

Standardise by subtracting the mean and dividing by the standard deviation.

P(no-one has guessed correctly) = $P\left(Z < \dfrac{4.5 - 24}{\sqrt{24}}\right) + P\left(Z \geqslant \dfrac{30.5 - 24}{\sqrt{24}}\right)$

$= P(Z < -3.980) + P(Z \geqslant 1.327)$

By symmetry, $P(Z < -3.980) = P(Z > 3.980) = 1 - P(Z < 3.980)$

The Normal tables only go up to $z = 3.49$, this is because $P(Z \leqslant 3.49)$ is so near 1 that 4 figure tables cannot show the difference. So $P(Z < -3.980) \approx 0$.

$P(Z \geqslant 1.327) = 1 - P(Z \leqslant 1.327)$
$= 1 - 0.9077$
$= 0.0923$

(add)

z	.02	6	7
1.3	9066	10	11

$9066 + 11 = 9077$

The probability that no-one guesses correctly is 0.092 (to 3 d.p.).

LINKS

Statistics   Chi-squared Test for Goodness of Fit (S3).

Test Yourself ▷L

1 Three of the following statements are false and one is true. Find the one that is true.

$X \sim$ Poisson(4).

A The Normal distribution with mean 4 and standard deviation 4 is a good approximation for X.

B The Normal distribution with mean 4 and standard deviation 2 is a good approximation for X.

C The Normal distribution with mean 4 and standard deviation 16 is a good approximation for X.

D X cannot be approximated by a Normal distribution because the mean is too small.

2 Day-long fishing trips are on offer at a seaside resort. The mean number of fish caught on such trips is 38. Assuming that the number of fish caught has a Poisson distribution, use a suitable approximating distribution to find the probability that fewer than 30 fish will be caught. (Answers are given to 3 d.p.)

A 0.084   B 0.097   C 0.112   D 0.411   E 0.916

This information is for questions 3 and 4.

A shop sells light bulbs. Past experience shows that the number of customers who want a particular kind of light bulb follows a Poisson distribution. The mean number of customers per week who want this kind of light bulb is 18.2.

3 Use a suitable approximating distribution to find the probability that at least 21 customers will want this particular kind of light bulb in a week. (Answers are given to 3 d.p.)

A 0.220   B 0.256   C 0.295   D 0.450   E 0.705

4 Use a suitable approximating distribution to find the probability that between 10 and 25 customers (inclusive) will want that kind of light bulb in a week. (Answers are given to 3 d.p.)

A 0.023   B 0.909   C 0.917   D 0.921   E 0.936

Exam-Style Question ▷L

A website manager finds that the mean number of people accessing the site per day is 44.8.

Assume that the Poisson distribution provides a suitable model for X, the number of people accessing the website in a day.

i)   Find the probability that exactly 50 people visit the website in one day.

ii) Use a suitable approximating distribution to find the probability that more than 50 people access the website in one day.

Samples and hypothesis testing

Sampling distribution of sample means from a Normal distribution

A ABOUT THIS TOPIC

Users of statistics often work with samples taken from larger populations. The mean of the sample might be expected to be near the population mean but how near could it be? Knowing how possible values of the sample mean are distributed is essential for conducting a Normal hypothesis test so this section is an introduction to the next two sections.

R REMEMBER

- If a random variable, X, has a Normal distribution with mean μ and standard deviation σ, this can be written as $X \sim N(\mu, \sigma^2)$.
- To use standard Normal tables, Normal variables have to be standardised by subtracting the mean and then dividing by the standard deviation.
- How to calculate sample mean and sample variance from S1.
  Variance, $s^2 = \dfrac{S_{xx}}{n-1}$ where $S_{xx} = \sum x^2 - n\bar{x}^2$.
- How to work with probabilities from S1.

K KEY FACTS

- For samples of size n from $N(\mu, \sigma^2)$ the sample mean is Normally distributed with mean μ and variance $\dfrac{\sigma^2}{n}$, i.e. $\bar{X} \sim N\left(\mu, \dfrac{\sigma^2}{n}\right)$.

- If the population variance (or standard deviation) is not known then the sample variance can be used as an estimate, as long as n is large. In that case, $\bar{X} \sim N\left(\mu, \dfrac{s^2}{n}\right)$.

What is the sampling distribution of the sample mean?

If a random sample of a given size, say 5, is taken from a Normal distribution with mean 30 and variance 9 then you would expect the sample mean to be somewhere near 30. Sometimes it might be a bit less than 30 and sometimes it might be a bit more than 30. The sample means for a large number of such samples are shown in the histogram.

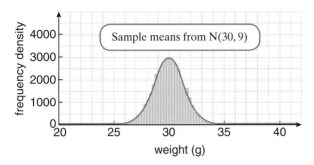

It looks as though the sample means are Normally distributed and that is, in fact, the case. The distribution of the sample means has mean 30 and variance $\frac{9}{5} = 1.8$.

A ADVICE

For samples of size n from $N(\mu, \sigma^2)$ the sample mean is Normally distributed with mean μ and variance $\frac{\sigma^2}{n}$, i.e. $\overline{X} \sim N\left(\mu, \frac{\sigma^2}{n}\right)$. This is called the **sampling distribution** of the sample means.

EXAMPLE 1

Gherkins have a mean weight of 30 g. Assume that the weight of a randomly chosen gherkin is Normally distributed with standard deviation 3 g. A jar of gherkins contains 15 gherkins. What is the distribution of the mean of the weights of the gherkins in a jar? Assume that the gherkins in a jar are a random sample.

SOLUTION

Let X be the weight, in grams, of a randomly chosen gherkin.
$X \sim N(30, 3^2)$

> Summarise the information in the question. Remember the variance is the square of the standard deviation.

Samples are of size 15 so $n = 15$.
The distribution of the sample mean, $\overline{X}$, is $\overline{X} \sim N\left(30, \frac{3^2}{15}\right)$, i.e. $N(30, 0.6)$.

> Upper case $\overline{X}$ stands for the general sample mean, lower case $\overline{x}$ would stand for a particular value.

A ADVICE

Notice that for larger sample sizes from the same population, the variance of the sample mean is smaller. This fits in with the intuition that larger samples should give a more reliable estimate of the population mean.

Information from samples

Samples are often taken to give information about likely values of population parameters, such as the population mean.

	True population value (this may be unknown)	Estimated value from the sample
Mean	μ	$\bar{x} = \dfrac{\sum x}{n}$
Variance for individual values	σ^2	$s^2 = \dfrac{\sum x^2 - n\bar{x}^2}{n - 1}$
Variance for samples of size n	$\dfrac{\sigma^2}{n}$	$\dfrac{s^2}{n}$

A ADVICE

If you are taking a sample from a population to find out about the population mean then it may be the case that you do not know the population standard deviation. If the sample size is large enough then the sample standard deviation can be used as an estimate of the population standard deviation. Samples with at least 50 data values are usually large enough but the estimate can be reasonable for 30, or more.

EXAMPLE 2

A particular species of fish is being studied by fishery experts. They catch a random sample of 150 fish from this species and measure the length, x cm, of each. Here is a summary of the data:

$$\sum x = 2\,405.9, \qquad \sum x^2 = 41\,531.08, \qquad \bar{x} = 16.039 \text{ (3 d.p.)}.$$

i) Find the sample variance.

ii) The population mean for this species used to be 16.50 cm. If the population mean is still 16.50 cm, what is the probability of getting a sample mean less than 16.04 cm when taking a sample of 150 fish?

SOLUTION

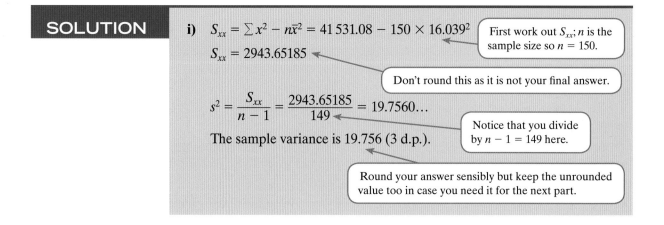

i) $S_{xx} = \sum x^2 - n\bar{x}^2 = 41\,531.08 - 150 \times 16.039^2$

First work out S_{xx}; n is the sample size so $n = 150$.

$S_{xx} = 2943.65185$

Don't round this as it is not your final answer.

$s^2 = \dfrac{S_{xx}}{n - 1} = \dfrac{2943.65185}{149} = 19.7560\ldots$

Notice that you divide by $n - 1 = 149$ here.

The sample variance is 19.756 (3 d.p.).

Round your answer sensibly but keep the unrounded value too in case you need it for the next part.

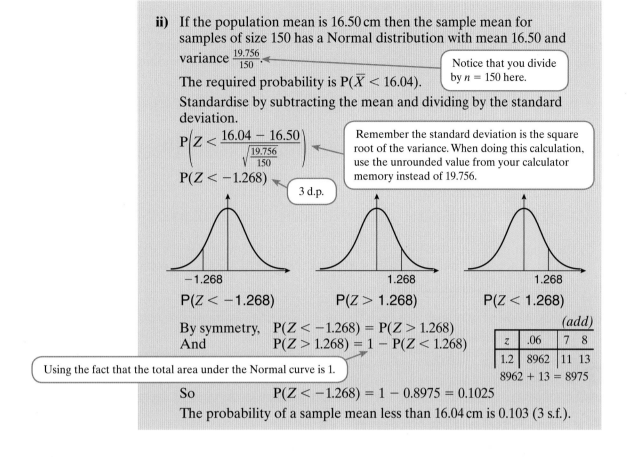

ii) If the population mean is 16.50 cm then the sample mean for samples of size 150 has a Normal distribution with mean 16.50 and variance $\frac{19.756}{150}$.

> Notice that you divide by $n = 150$ here.

The required probability is $P(\overline{X} < 16.04)$.

Standardise by subtracting the mean and dividing by the standard deviation.

$$P\left(Z < \frac{16.04 - 16.50}{\sqrt{\frac{19.756}{150}}}\right)$$

> Remember the standard deviation is the square root of the variance. When doing this calculation, use the unrounded value from your calculator memory instead of 19.756.

$P(Z < -1.268)$

> 3 d.p.

| $P(Z < -1.268)$ | $P(Z > 1.268)$ | $P(Z < 1.268)$ |

By symmetry, $P(Z < -1.268) = P(Z > 1.268)$

And $P(Z > 1.268) = 1 - P(Z < 1.268)$

> Using the fact that the total area under the Normal curve is 1.

(add)

z	.06	7	8
1.2	8962	11	13

$8962 + 13 = 8975$

So $P(Z < -1.268) = 1 - 0.8975 = 0.1025$

The probability of a sample mean less than 16.04 cm is 0.103 (3 s.f.).

⚠ The variance of the sample mean is the population variance divided by n, $\frac{\sigma^2}{n}$.

The standard deviation of the sample mean is the square root of this variance, $\sqrt{\frac{\sigma^2}{n}} = \frac{\sigma}{\sqrt{n}}$; it is not the population standard deviation divided by n.

LINKS

Statistics   Hypothesis Tests using the Normal Distribution (S2);
Confidence Intervals using the Normal Distribution (S3);
Central Limit Theorem (S3).

Test Yourself ▶L

1 Random samples of size 5 are taken from $N(12, 2.5)$. What is the distribution of the mean of such samples?

   A $N(2.4, 0.5)$ B $N(12, 0.5)$ C $N(12, 0.1)$

   D $N(12, 2.5)$ E $N(60, 12.5)$

2 Random samples of size 4 are taken from $N(5, 0.81)$. What is the standard deviation of the distribution of sample means?

   A 0.2025   B 0.225   C 2.5   D 0.45   E 0.9

This information is for questions 3 and 4.

Peppers are sold in packs of three. The weights of individual peppers which are packaged in this way are Normally distributed with mean 135 g and standard deviation 9.3 g. Assume that the three peppers in a pack are chosen at random.

3 What is the probability that the mean weight of the peppers in a pack is less than 130 g? (Answers are given to 3 d.p.)

A 0.053   B 0.176   C 0.295   D 0.431   E 0.824

4 Only 5% of packs contain peppers with a mean weight over m g. Find the value of m. (Answers are given to 1 d.p.)

A 139.5   B 140.1   C 142.0   D 143.8   E 150.3

5 The time, x minutes, taken by each of a sample of 60 students to complete an exercise is noted. Guidance notes say that an average student should take 15 minutes to complete the exercise.

The results are summarised as follows:

$$\sum x = 881.13, \qquad \sum x^2 = 13\,371.45.$$

What is the sample variance? (Answers are given to 2 d.p.).

A -2.18 B 2.70   C 3.60   D 7.19   E 7.32

Exam-Style Question ⅫL

John Bridges is a long jumper. The distance he jumps, X m, is Normally distributed with mean 5.35 and standard deviation 0.1.

He jumps three times in a competition.

Find the probability that:

i) his first attempt is longer than 5.4 m

ii) at least one of his attempts is longer than 5.4 m

iii) the mean of his three attempts is longer than 5.4 m.

One-tail hypothesis test for the mean using the Normal distribution

A | ABOUT THIS TOPIC

A simple example will illustrate the ideas in this section. A quality control inspector in a battery factory needs to make sure that the batteries will work for an acceptable length of time. The batteries should last for 7.4 hours, on average; so he tests a sample to see if the average time they last for is near enough to 7.4 hours. Knowing the distribution of the sample means gives a way of deciding whether it is near enough to 7.4 hours. These techniques can be used in a wide range of situations – not just for batteries!

R | REMEMBER

- To use standard Normal tables, Normal variables have to be standardised by subtracting the mean and then dividing by the standard deviation.
- For samples of size n from $N(\mu, \sigma^2)$ the sample mean is Normally distributed with mean μ and variance $\dfrac{\sigma^2}{n}$. i.e. $\bar{X} \sim N\left(\mu, \dfrac{\sigma^2}{n}\right)$.
- If the population variance (or standard deviation) is not known then the sample standard deviation, s, can be used as an estimate for σ, as long as n is large. In that case, $\bar{X} \sim N\left(\mu, \dfrac{s^2}{n}\right)$.

K | KEY FACTS

- The null hypothesis for a test using the Normal distribution is that the population mean, μ, takes a particular value, e.g. $H_0 : \mu = 7.4$.

- For a one-tail test, the alternative hypothesis corresponding to the null hypothesis above would be **either** $H_1 : \mu > 7.4$ **or** $H_1 : \mu < 7.4$.

- To conduct the test, a random sample of size n is taken and the sample mean, $\bar{x}$, is found.

- If the population has a Normal distribution with standard deviation σ, the test statistic for the null hypothesis given above is $z = \dfrac{\bar{x} - 7.4}{\dfrac{\sigma}{\sqrt{n}}}$. If the null hypothesis is true, this has a standard Normal distribution, with mean 0 and standard deviation 1.

- Standard Normal tables and the significance level are used to decide whether the test statistic is near enough to zero for the null hypothesis to be plausible.

EXAMPLE 1

A factory makes a variety of battery which it claims has a mean lifetime of 7.4 hours of continuous use. The factory has changed one of its suppliers. The quality control inspector is concerned that the mean life for batteries could have been reduced. The inspector takes a sample of 5 batteries and tests how long they last for. The times, in hours, are:

$$7.02 \qquad 6.43 \qquad 7.35 \qquad 7.97 \qquad 7.92$$

i) State suitable null and alternative hypotheses for a test.

ii) Carry out the test at the 5% level of significance.

Assume that battery life is Normally distributed with standard deviation 0.6 hours.

SOLUTION

i) $H_0: \mu = 7.4$ where μ is the mean battery life in hours for the population of batteries made by the factory.

$$H_1: \mu < 7.4$$

> The inspector suspects that the mean battery life could be reduced so the alternative hypothesis is that μ is less than 7.4.

A | ADVICE

The null hypothesis for this type of test is always that μ = a particular value. You should say that μ stands for the population mean; there is often a mark for doing so but do remember to say what the population is in the context of the question. Just saying 'μ is the population mean' with no further explanation is not enough.

ii)

What to do	What to write down for this example
If the null hypothesis is true, write down the distribution the sample mean comes from. Remember, for a sample of size n from $N(\mu, \sigma^2)$ the sample mean, $\overline{X}$, has a Normal distribution with mean μ and variance $\dfrac{\sigma^2}{n}$.	If H_0 is true, $\overline{X} \sim N\left(7.4, \dfrac{0.6^2}{5}\right)$ > You were told to assume that the standard deviation for individual batteries is 0.6. There were 5 batteries in the sample.
Work out the sample mean.	$\overline{x} = \dfrac{7.02 + 6.43 + 7.35 + 7.97 + 7.92}{5}$ $= \dfrac{36.69}{5} = 7.338$
Calculate the test statistic, standardising so that you can use Normal tables. (Subtract the mean and divide by the standard deviation). $Z = \dfrac{\overline{X} - \mu}{\sqrt{\dfrac{\sigma^2}{n}}}$ has a standard Normal distribution, $N(0, 1)$.	$z = \dfrac{\overline{x} - \mu}{\sqrt{\dfrac{\sigma^2}{n}}}$ $z = \dfrac{7.338 - 7.4}{\sqrt{\dfrac{0.6^2}{5}}} = -0.231\ldots$
Is it a one or two-tail test? You will be able to tell from the form of the alternative hypothesis.	One-tail test > The inspector is only concerned about the possibility of μ being less than 7.4

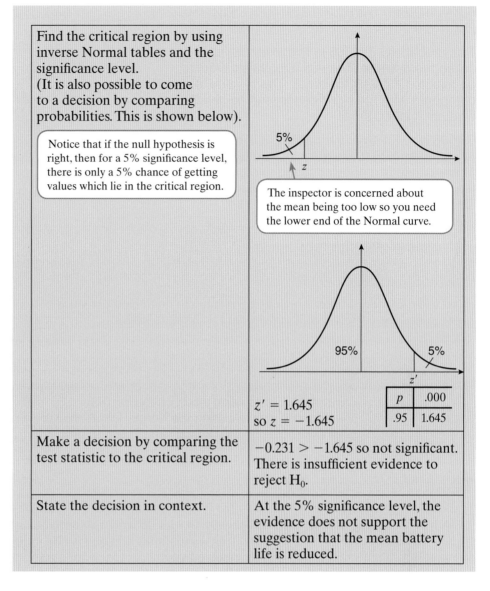

Find the critical region by using inverse Normal tables and the significance level.
(It is also possible to come to a decision by comparing probabilities. This is shown below).

> Notice that if the null hypothesis is right, then for a 5% significance level, there is only a 5% chance of getting values which lie in the critical region.

5%

z

> The inspector is concerned about the mean being too low so you need the lower end of the Normal curve.

95%   5%

z'

$z' = 1.645$
so $z = -1.645$

p	.000
.95	1.645

| Make a decision by comparing the test statistic to the critical region. | $-0.231 > -1.645$ so not significant. There is insufficient evidence to reject H_0. |
| State the decision in context. | At the 5% significance level, the evidence does not support the suggestion that the mean battery life is reduced. |

A ADVICE

There is often a mark given at the end of the question for stating the decision in context so don't just stop with 'accept H_0' or 'reject H_0'. Remember that you cannot say definitely whether the null hypothesis is true or false. Phrases like 'at the 5% significance level, the evidence does not support …' or 'there is sufficient evidence at the 5% level that …' are useful.

Using probability instead of a critical region

Using Example 1, the working would the same as in the table above, until the stage noting whether it is a one-tail or a two-tail test.

Instead of finding a critical region, find the probability of the test statistic being below the calculated value.

> The inspector is concerned that the mean may be too low.

$P(Z < -0.231) = P(Z > 0.231) = 1 - P(Z < 0.231)$
$P(Z < -0.231) = 1 - 0.5914 = 0.4086$

This probability (0.4086 in this example) is called the **p-value**. The null hypothesis would be rejected if it was too small. The p-value is compared with the significance level to decide whether it is too small.

0.4086 is not a small probability; it is much bigger than 0.05 (the significance level). There is insufficient evidence to reject H_0. It is reasonable to conclude that the mean battery life is not reduced.

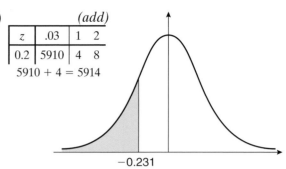

(add)

z	.03	1	2
0.2	5910	4	8

$5910 + 4 = 5914$

-0.231

A ADVICE

You can use either a critical region or a p-value to do a hypothesis test but you should understand how to find the critical region in case you are asked to do so.

LINKS

Statistics   Hypothesis Tests using the t Distribution (S3); Confidence Intervals using the Normal Distribution or the t Distribution (S3); Central Limit Theorem (S3).

Test Yourself ⊃L

1 A man has found that the time it takes him to walk to work is Normally distributed with mean 15.5 minutes. After going on a fitness course, he thinks that he may be walking faster on average now. Which are suitable null and alternative hypotheses to use for a test?

A $H_0 : \mu = 15.5$ **B** $H_0 : \mu = 15.5$ **C** $H_0 : \mu = 15.5$ **D** $H_0 : \mu < 15.5$ **E** $H_0 : \mu > 15.5$
    $H_1 : \mu < 15.5$ $H_1 : \mu > 15.5$ $H_1 : \mu \neq 15.5$ $H_1 : \mu > 15.5$ $H_1 : \mu < 15.5$

2 Which is the best description of the meaning of μ in the hypotheses in question 1?

  A The critical value.

  B His new mean walking time, in minutes, after the fitness course.

  C The mean of a random sample of his walking times, in minutes, after the fitness course.

  D The population mean.

  E The test statistic.

The following information is for questions 3, 4 and 5.

A particular breed of hen produces eggs with a mean weight of 42.5 g and standard deviation 4.2 g. A new diet is used for a flock of these hens. The mean weight of a random sample of 20 eggs is 43.9 g. Test at the 2% level whether this provides evidence that the mean weight of eggs has increased. Assume that egg weights are Normally distributed with standard deviation 4.2 g.

3 For the test described above, what is the critical region?

    A $z \leqslant 0.02$ **B** $z > 0.8365$ **C** $z > 1.645$ **D** $z > 2.054$ **E** $z > 42.5$

4 For the test described above, what is the test statistic? (Answers are given to 3 decimal places).

   A $z = 0.333$ **B** $z = 1.491$ **C** $z = 1.587$ **D** $z = 6.667$

Make sure you have the right answers to questions 3 and 4 before doing question 5.

5 What is the final conclusion for the test described above?

   A The test statistic is in the critical region so it is reasonable to conclude that the mean weight of an egg has increased.

   B The test statistic is in the critical region so there is insufficient evidence to conclude that the mean weight of an egg has increased.

   C The test statistic is not in the critical region so it is reasonable to conclude that the mean weight of an egg has increased.

   D The test statistic is not in the critical region so there is insufficient evidence to conclude that the mean weight of an egg has increased.

Exam-Style Question ⊃L

A national survey finds that the heights of men are Normally distributed with mean 176 cm and standard deviation 6.7 cm.

A historian is studying army records and he suspects that the soldiers he is studying were shorter, on average.

A random sample from the records gives the following heights of soldiers (all in cm):

   165   158   169   176   175   179   172

i) Write down suitable null and alternative hypotheses to test the historian's suspicion.

ii) Assume that the standard deviation of the heights of soldiers is 6.7 cm. Carry out a suitable hypothesis test, at the 5% level of significance, to test the historian's suspicion. You should state your conclusions clearly.

Two-tail hypothesis test for the mean using the Normal distribution

A ABOUT THIS TOPIC

This section follows on from the last one. In a one-tail test you are looking for evidence of either an increase or a decrease but not both. In a two-tail test, you are looking for evidence of any difference.

R REMEMBER

- To use standard Normal tables, Normal variables have to be standardised by subtracting the mean and then dividing by the standard deviation.
- For samples of size n from $N(\mu, \sigma^2)$ the sample mean is Normally distributed with mean μ and variance $\dfrac{\sigma^2}{n}$. i.e. $\overline{X} \sim N\left(\mu, \dfrac{\sigma^2}{n}\right)$.
- If the population variance (or standard deviation) is not known then the sample standard deviation, s, can be used as an estimate, as long as n is large. In that case, $\overline{X} \sim N\left(\mu, \dfrac{s^2}{n}\right)$.
- How to calculate sample mean and sample variance from S1.
  Variance, $s^2 = \dfrac{S_{xx}}{n-1}$ where $S_{xx} = \sum x^2 - n\overline{x}^2$.

K KEY FACTS

- The null hypothesis for a test using the Normal distribution is that the population mean, μ, takes a particular value, e. g. $H_0 : \mu = 7.4$.

- For a two-tail test, the alternative hypothesis corresponding to the null hypothesis above would be $H_1 : \mu \neq 7.4$.

- To conduct the test, a random sample of size n is taken and the sample mean, $\overline{x}$, is found.

- If the population has a Normal distribution with standard deviation σ, the test statistic for the null hypothesis given above is $z = \dfrac{\overline{x} - 7.4}{\frac{\sigma}{\sqrt{n}}}$. If the null hypothesis is true, this standardised distribution is Normal with mean 0 and standard deviation 1.

- Standard Normal tables and the significance level are used to decide whether the test statistic is near enough to zero for the null hypothesis to be plausible.

EXAMPLE 1

The mean wingspan of a particular species of butterfly is 6.2 cm. The standard deviation is 0.3 cm. A zoologist suspects that the mean wingspan for this species in a particular region has changed due to environmental factors. A sample of 10 butterflies is measured, the mean wingspan for the sample is 6.38 cm. Test at the 1% level of significance whether this provides evidence of a change in mean wingspan. Assume that the standard deviation is still 0.3 cm and that wingspans are Normally distributed. State your hypotheses and conclusions carefully.

SOLUTION

$H_0 : \mu = 6.2$ ⎱ where μ is the mean wingspan in cm for the population of
$H_1 : \mu \neq 6.2$ ⎰ butterflies in the region.

> The zoologist is looking for evidence of a change.

Let X be the wingspan of a randomly chosen butterfly in cm.
If the null hypothesis is true, $X \sim N(6.2, 0.3^2)$.

The distribution of the sample means is $\bar{X} \sim N\left(6.2, \dfrac{0.3^2}{10}\right)$.

> The sample size, n, is 10.

The test statistic is $z = \dfrac{\bar{x} - \mu}{\sqrt{\dfrac{\sigma^2}{n}}} = \dfrac{6.38 - 6.2}{\sqrt{\dfrac{0.3^2}{10}}} = 1.8973\ldots$

> You were told that the sample mean was 6.38 cm so $\bar{x} = 6.38$. There were 10 butterflies in the sample so $n = 10$.

> ⚠ Don't get confused between the sample mean, $\bar{x}$, and the population mean, μ.

The zoologist is looking for evidence of a change in either direction so it is a two-tail test.

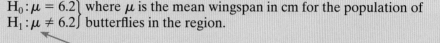

0.5% 99% 0.5% 0.995 0.005
$-z$ z z

> The significance level is 1% and it is a two-tail test, so 0.5% for each tail.

> The probability below the right hand tail is 0.995.

The critical value is $z = 2.576$.
The test statistic, $1.8973\ldots$, is not in the critical region so there is insufficient evidence to reject H_0.

p	.000	.005
.99	2.326	2.576

> Only values of the test statistic that are bigger than 2.576 or smaller than -2.576 would provide enough evidence to reject the null hypothesis.

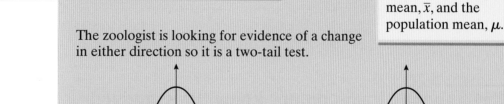

0.5% 99% 0.5%
-2.576 2.576

At the 1% significance level, there is insufficient evidence that the mean wingspan for this species of butterfly in this region has changed from 6.2 cm.

A ADVICE

For a two-tail test half the significance level goes in each tail. Always draw a Normal diagram to help you see what you should look up in inverse Normal tables.

EXAMPLE 2

What would the sample mean need to be in Example 1 for there to be sufficient evidence to reject the null hypothesis?

SOLUTION

To reject the null hypothesis, the standardised sample mean, $z = \dfrac{\bar{x} - \mu}{\sqrt{\dfrac{\sigma^2}{n}}}$, must either be more than 2.576 or less than -2.576.

Left hand tail	Right hand tail
You do not know what the sample mean is in this example; you are trying to find out what it needs to be.	
$\dfrac{\bar{x} - \mu}{\sqrt{\dfrac{\sigma^2}{n}}} < -2.576$	$\dfrac{\bar{x} - \mu}{\sqrt{\dfrac{\sigma^2}{n}}} > 2.576$
$\dfrac{\bar{x} - 6.2}{\sqrt{\dfrac{0.3^2}{10}}} < -2.576$	$\dfrac{\bar{x} - 6.2}{\sqrt{\dfrac{0.3^2}{10}}} > 2.576$
$\bar{x} - 6.2 < -0.2443\ldots$	$\bar{x} - 6.2 > 0.2443\ldots$
$\bar{x} < 5.9556$ (4 d.p.)	$\bar{x} > 6.4444$ (4 d.p.)

The sample mean would have to be either greater than 6.4444 or less than 5.9556 for the null hypothesis to be rejected.

What happens if you do not know the standard deviation?

In Example 1, you were told to assume that the standard deviation was unchanged (0.3 cm). You may come across situations where you know that the distribution is Normal but you do not know the standard deviation. In that case, the sample standard deviation can be used as an estimate of the population standard deviation, if the sample size is large enough (50 is usually large enough).

EXAMPLE 3

A variety of mussel usually has a mean shell length of 67 mm. Shell lengths are normally distributed. A sample of 80 mussels from a particular bay are measured. The lengths, x mm, are summarised:

$$\sum x = 5\,132, \qquad \sum x^2 = 341\,020, \qquad \bar{x} = 64.15$$

Test at the 5% significance level whether there is evidence that mussels from this bay have a mean length which differs from 67 mm.

SOLUTION

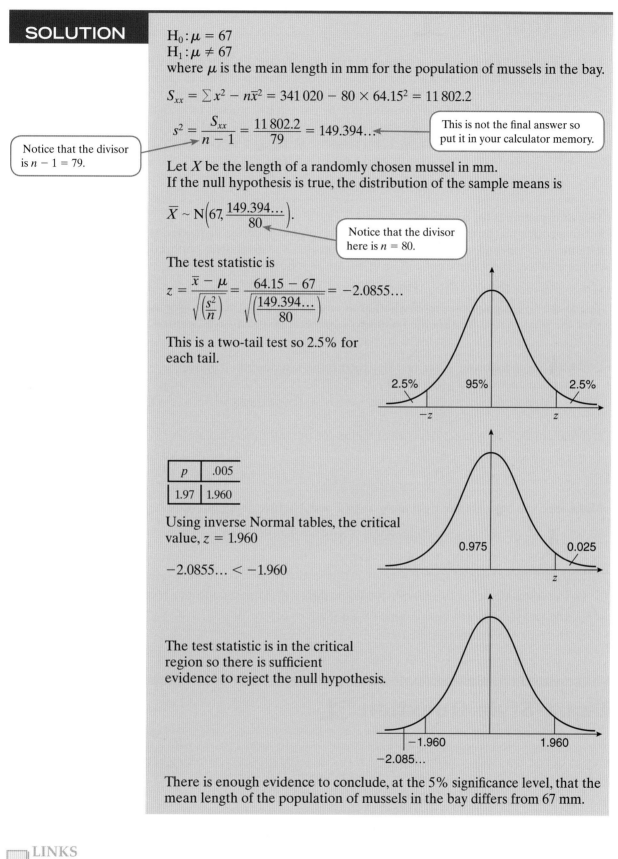

$H_0 : \mu = 67$
$H_1 : \mu \neq 67$
where μ is the mean length in mm for the population of mussels in the bay.

$S_{xx} = \sum x^2 - n\bar{x}^2 = 341\,020 - 80 \times 64.15^2 = 11\,802.2$

$s^2 = \dfrac{S_{xx}}{n-1} = \dfrac{11\,802.2}{79} = 149.394\ldots$

> **This is not the final answer so put it in your calculator memory.**

> **Notice that the divisor is $n - 1 = 79$.**

Let X be the length of a randomly chosen mussel in mm.
If the null hypothesis is true, the distribution of the sample means is

$\bar{X} \sim N\left(67, \dfrac{149.394\ldots}{80}\right).$

> **Notice that the divisor here is $n = 80$.**

The test statistic is

$z = \dfrac{\bar{x} - \mu}{\sqrt{\left(\dfrac{s^2}{n}\right)}} = \dfrac{64.15 - 67}{\sqrt{\left(\dfrac{149.394\ldots}{80}\right)}} = -2.0855\ldots$

This is a two-tail test so 2.5% for each tail.

2.5%   95%   2.5%

$-z$ z

p	.005
1.97	1.960

Using inverse Normal tables, the critical value, $z = 1.960$

$-2.0855\ldots < -1.960$

0.975   0.025

z

The test statistic is in the critical region so there is sufficient evidence to reject the null hypothesis.

-1.960 1.960

$-2.085\ldots$

There is enough evidence to conclude, at the 5% significance level, that the mean length of the population of mussels in the bay differs from 67 mm.

LINKS

Statistics

Hypothesis Tests using the t Distribution (S3);
Confidence Intervals using the Normal Distribution or
the t Distribution (S3); Central Limit Theorem (S3).

Test Yourself

1 The systolic blood pressure of women in the UK is Normally distributed with mean 121 mmHg. A researcher wants to know whether a particular diet changes the mean blood pressure of women on it. A sample of 50 women on the diet is taken; the mean blood pressure of the sample of 50 women is 126.6 mmHg. Which of the following are the correct hypotheses for a significance test? (μ is the mean systolic blood pressure for the whole population of UK women on the diet).

A $H_0 : \mu = 121$ B $H_0 : \mu = 121$ C $H_0 : \mu = 126.6$ D $H_0 : \mu = 126.6$
    $H_1 : \mu > 121$ $H_1 : \mu \neq 121$ $H_1 : \mu < 126.6$ $H_1 : \mu \neq 126.6$

E There is no need for a hypothesis test because $126.6 \neq 121$.

This information is for questions 2, 3 and 4.

When a coffee machine is working properly, the volume of coffee dispensed is Normally distributed with mean 175 ml and standard deviation 6.4 ml. After the machine is serviced, a sample of 10 cups of coffee is taken. The volumes of coffee, in ml, are as follows:

178   172   182   188   188   191   166   179   187   173

Test at the 10% significance level whether the mean amount of coffee dispensed differs from 175 ml after the service. Assume that the volumes of coffee are Normally distributed with standard deviation 6.4 ml.

2 Which of the following is the test statistic for the test described above? (Rounded answers are given to 4 d.p.)

A $z = 0.8438$ B $z = 1.3184$ C $z = 2.6682$ D $z = 8.4375$

3 Which of the following is the critical region for the test described above?

A $z > 0.8289$ or $z < -0.8289$ B $z > 0.9962$ or $z < -0.9962$
C $z > 1.282$ or $z < -1.282$ D $z > 1.645$ or $z < -1.645$

Make sure you have got the right answers to 2 and 3 before doing question 4.

4 Which one of the following statements is true for the test described above?

A The test statistic is in the critical region.

B If another sample of size 10 was taken, the critical region could have been different.

C The test statistic for this sample would be different if the significance level was 2%.

D The test statistic will be the same for all samples of size 10.

E The null hypothesis must be false.

Exam-Style Question

When a biscuit production line is working correctly it produces biscuits with a mean mass of 20 g. The masses of biscuits are Normally distributed. To check the process is working correctly, a random sample of 60 biscuits is taken and the mass, x g, of each biscuit is measured.

The results are summarised as follows.

$n = 60$, $\sum x = 1181.4$, $\sum x^2 = 23\,315.38$

i) Calculate the mean and standard deviation of the data.

ii) State suitable null and alternative hypotheses for a test to see whether the mean mass of biscuits produced has changed.

iii) Carry out the test, at the 5% significance level, stating your conclusions carefully.

The χ^2 test for independence in a contingency table

A · ABOUT THIS TOPIC

A ABOUT THIS TOPIC

A contingency table shows information about two variables (usually categorical). A chi-squared test assesses whether the variables are independent or whether there is some association between them. This method is used in many areas of study including social and biological sciences.

R REMEMBER

- Two-way tables from S1.
- The general idea and terminology of hypothesis testing from S1 or from the previous sections.

K KEY FACTS

- An $r \times c$ contingency table contains observed frequencies in r rows and c columns.
- The expected frequency for each cell is $\dfrac{\text{row total} \times \text{column total}}{\text{total sample size}}$.
- The null hypothesis is that there is no association between the variables. The alternative hypothesis is that there is some association.
- The test statistic is $X^2 = \sum \dfrac{(f_o - f_e)^2}{f_e}$ where f_o is the observed frequency in each cell and f_e is the expected frequency.
- There are $v = (r - 1)(c - 1)$ degrees of freedom for the test.

Contingency tables

A contingency table shows the relationship between two variables. The variables are either categorical or grouped, e.g. the annual salaries of a random sample of full-time employees could be reported in a two-way table like the one here. Each cell shows the frequency of that group.

	Minimum wage	Low	Medium	High
Men	7	20	48	17
Women	26	37	46	2

The question of whether there is a relationship between gender and earnings might arise. A χ^2 test is one way to investigate whether there is such a relationship.

The null hypothesis is that there is no association between the variables. The alternative hypothesis is that there is some association.

EXAMPLE 1   For the data in the table above, test at the 5% level whether there is association between gender and earnings.

SOLUTION

H_0: There is no association between gender and earnings
H_1: There is some association between gender and earnings

> Start by stating the null and alternative hypotheses; notice that they are in words for a χ^2 test and that they refer to the specific variables in this question.

Observed, f_o	Minimum wage	Low	Medium	High	Row totals
Men	7	20	48	17	92
Women	26	37	46	2	111
Column totals	33	57	94	19	203

A ADVICE

- You will need the row and column totals for the contingency table.
- The easiest way to show your working is in three tables:
  - observed frequencies
  - expected frequencies
  - contributions to the test statistic.

The expected frequency for each cell is
$$\frac{\text{row total} \times \text{column total}}{\text{total sample size}}.$$

> This is because the expected frequency is proportional to row total and column total.

Expected, f_e	Minimum wage	Low	Medium	High	Row totals
Men	14.9557	25.8325	42.6010	8.6108	92
Women	18.0443	31.1675	51.3990	10.3892	111
Column totals	33	57	94	19	203

$$\frac{111 \times 33}{203}$$

⚠ The expected frequency need not be a whole number. You will be using it in the next stage of working so do not round it too much.

A ADVICE

The row and column totals are the same for the expected frequencies as they are for the observed frequencies. Do not waste time in an examination checking this but do look out for obviously wrong answers.

The test statistic for the χ^2 test is $X^2 = \sum \frac{(f_o - f_e)^2}{f_e}$ where f_o is the observed frequency in each cell and f_e is the expected frequency.

The next table will show the contributions to the test statistic. Each contribution is $\dfrac{(f_o - f_e)^2}{f_e}$.

For the 'Men, minimum wage' cell this works out to be

$$\frac{(7 - 14.9557)^2}{14.9557} = 4.232...$$

Contribution to test statistic	Minimum wage	Low	Medium	High	Row totals
Men	4.2320	1.3169	0.6842	8.1732	14.4063
Women	3.5076	1.0915	0.5671	6.7742	11.9402
				Total	26.3465

$\dfrac{(26 - 18.0443)^2}{18.0443}$. The unrounded value has been used in the calculation. You might not have enough memories on your calculator to put all the unrounded observed frequencies in them. In that case, you can fill in the second and third tables at the same time.

You do not need the column totals as well as the row totals in this table as you only want the overall total of the cells.

The test statistic is $X^2 = 26.347$ (to 3 d.p.).

Notice that a letter from the English alphabet is used for the test statistic; you have come across this already: in the Normal test for μ, the test statistic is z.

There are $v = (r - 1)(c - 1)$ degrees of freedom for the test. r is the number of rows and c is the number of columns.
$v = (2 - 1)(4 - 1) = 3$
Critical value $= 7.815$
$26.347 > 7.815$

You need to work out the number of degrees of freedom to see which row of the tables to use to find the critical value.

Compare the test statistic with the critical value then reach a decision.

The critical value tells you how big X^2 needs to be for you to reject the null hypothesis

$p\%$	5.0
$v = 1$	3.841
2	5.991
3	7.815

Remember to state your final conclusion in the context of the original question.

Reject the null hypothesis at the 5% level.
There seems to be some association between gender and earnings.

One-tail or two-tail?

For other statistical tests you have encountered in S1 and S2 you have had to decide whether to do a one-tail test or a two-tail test. The question does not arise with a χ^2 test; this is because the test statistic involves squaring terms so it will always be positive. The χ^2 test is sometimes referred to as a one-sided test. You will see how the contributions to the test statistic can be analysed in the next section; this can give you information about the nature of the association.

LINKS

Statistics χ^2 Test for Goodness of Fit (S3).

Test Yourself ⊃L

Questions 1 to 4 are about this contingency table.

A sample of year 12 students are asked how often they read their horoscopes. They are also asked whether they are taking Mathematics AS. The results are summarised in the following table.

	Frequency of reading horoscope		
	Often	**Sometimes**	**Never**
AS Maths	5	25	10
No Maths	20	45	15

1 Which of the following is the null hypothesis for the χ^2 test on the contingency table?

 A Students who take AS Mathematics are less likely to read their horoscopes.

 B Students who often read their horoscopes are less likely to take AS Mathematics.

 C There is some association between taking AS Mathematics and reading horoscopes.

 D There is no association between taking AS Mathematics and reading horoscopes.

2 Which of the following is the test statistic for the χ^2 test on the contingency table? (Give your answer to 3 d.p.)

 A 0.256 B 2.649 C 2.679 D 3.414 E 33.333

3 How many degrees of freedom does the χ^2 test on the contingency table have?

 A 2 B 5 C 6 D 120

Make sure you have the right answers to questions 1 to 3 before doing question 4.

4 Which of the following is the correct conclusion for the χ^2 test on the contingency table at the 10% level of significance?

 A The test statistic is bigger than the critical value so accept the null hypothesis.

 B The test statistic is bigger than the critical value so reject the null hypothesis.

 C The test statistic is smaller than the critical value so there is a correlation between doing AS Mathematics and reading your horoscope.

 D The test statistic is smaller than the critical value so there is insufficient evidence to conclude that there is any association between doing AS Mathematics and reading your horoscope.

Exam-Style Question ⊃L

A magazine conducts a survey of a random sample of its readers to find out if they would be interested in subscribing to an internet version of the magazine. The results are summarised in the table below which shows the number of people in each category.

		Age				Row totals
		under 25	26–40	41–60	over 60	
Interest in subscribing to internet version?	Would subscribe	11	60	27	38	136
	Would not subscribe	45	113	56	50	264
Column totals		56	173	83	88	400

Conduct a test at the 5% level of significance to examine whether there is any association between age and interest in subscribing to the internet version. You should state your null and alternative hypotheses carefully.

Contributions to the χ^2 test statistic

This section follows on from the previous section. If a χ^2 test shows that there is some association then looking at the contribution that each cell in the contingency table makes to the test statistic gives more information about the type of association.

- χ^2 test for a contingency table from the previous section.
- The test statistic is $X^2 = \sum \dfrac{(f_o - f_e)^2}{f_e}$

  where f_o is the observed frequency in each cell and f_e is the expected frequency.

- If expected frequencies are too small, the χ^2 tables are not a good approximation for the distribution of the test statistic. Expected frequencies of 5 or more are fine.

- When looking at contributions to the test statistic, after performing the test:
  - Look for large contributions first – these are where observed and expected frequencies are far apart. Then look at whether the observed frequency of each cell is larger or smaller than the expected frequency of that cell.
  - Remember that expected frequencies were calculated on the assumption that there was no association between the variables, so large contributions show where the association is strongest.
  - Look for small contributions – these are where observed and expected frequencies are close together.

- It is best to show the contributions to the test statistic in a table so that the individual contributions can be seen.

 For small values of the expected frequency, the χ^2 test can be inaccurate. A rule of thumb which is often used is '5 or more' for **expected** frequencies (**not** observed frequencies). However, a χ^2 test is sometimes used on contingency tables with expected frequencies of less than 5.

EXAMPLE 1

Forty students were asked whether they had a part-time job. Find the expected frequencies for this contingency table. Why should you be cautious about using a χ^2 test on this table?

Observed, f_o	Female	Male	Total
Part-time job	22	6	28
No part-time job	7	5	12
Total	**29**	**11**	**40**

SOLUTION

Remember the expected frequency for each cell is
$$\frac{\text{row total} \times \text{column total}}{\text{total sample size}},$$
e.g. $\frac{28 \times 29}{40} = 20.3$.

Expected, f_e	Female	Male	Total
Part-time job	20.3	7.7	28
No part-time job	8.7	3.3	12
Total	29	11	40

You should be cautious about using a χ^2 test because one of the expected frequencies is less than 5.

A ADVICE

For some contingency tables you might be able to combine categories to get higher expected frequencies. For example, if there were a lot of age groups you might be able to combine two of them. It is not possible to combine categories in this table as there are only two categories for each variable.

Interpreting contributions to the χ^2 test statistic

If you find that there is association between the variables in a χ^2 test on a contingency table, you can explore the relationship by looking at the individual contributions to the test statistic.

- Look for large contributions first – these are where observed and expected frequencies are far apart. Then look at whether the observed frequency of each cell is larger or smaller than the expected frequency of that cell.
- Remember that expected frequencies were calculated on the assumption that there was no association between the variables so large contributions show where the association is strongest.
- Look for small contributions – these are where observed and expected frequencies are close together.

EXAMPLE 2

In Example 1 of the previous section, you found that there was an association between gender and earnings. The observed and expected frequencies and contributions to the test statistic are shown below. Discuss how gender and earnings are related.

Observed, f_o	Minimum wage	Low	Medium	High	Row totals
Men	7	20	48	17	92
Women	26	37	46	2	111
Column totals	33	57	94	19	203

Expected, f_e	Minimum wage	Low	Medium	High	Row totals
Men	14.9557	25.8325	42.6010	8.6108	92
Women	18.0443	31.1675	51.3990	10.3892	111
Column totals	33	57	94	19	203

Contribution to the test statistic	Minimum wage	Low	Medium	High	Row totals
Men	4.2320	1.3169	0.6842	8.1732	14.4063
Women	3.5076	1.0915	0.5671	6.7742	11.9402
				Total	26.3465

SOLUTION

The highest contributions to the test statistic, 8.1732 and 6.774, come from the highest earning group. There are more men and fewer women in this group than would be expected if there was no association.

> The observed frequency of women in this group is lower than the expected frequency; the observed frequency is higher than the expected frequency for men.

The next highest contributions, 4.2320 and 3.5076, are from the lowest earning group. Looking at observed and expected frequencies shows that there are more women and fewer men in this group than would be expected if there was no association.

The lowest contributions, 0.6842 and 0.5671, are from the medium earning group. In this group, women and men seem to be represented similarly to what would be expected if there was no association.

⚠ You must look at the contributions to the chi-squared statistic before looking at the differences between observed and expected frequencies. This will help you to see which differences are most significant.

A ADVICE

- When answering this kind of question don't just write a list of comments – start by saying what the size of the contribution to the test statistic is for that cell then comment on whether the observed frequency for that cell is larger or smaller than the expected frequency.
- It will usually be obvious in exam questions which are the big contributions and which are the small ones but, as a rule of thumb, you would usually consider a contribution of less than 1 as small.

LINKS

Statistics χ^2 Test for Goodness of Fit (S3).

Test Yourself ▶L

1 A sample of year 6 students is asked which of the three subjects, English, mathematics or science, they feel most confident about. The results are summarised in the following table.

Observed frequencies	Feel most confident about			Row total
	English	Mathematics	Science	
Boy	5	9	3	17
Girl	6	5	2	13
Column total	11	14	5	30

Which one of the following statements is true?

A The reason you can't use a χ^2 test on the data is that some of the observed frequencies are below 5.

B The best thing to do with the data would be to combine the English and science columns.

C The data show that boys are more confident about mathematics than girls.

D To use a χ^2 test, you really need data from a larger sample of students.

This information is for questions 2 and 3.
The Key Stage 1 mathematics results for 400 children are classified by whether the child receives free school meals or not. Observed and expected frequencies are shown below.

Observed, f_o		Key Stage 1 Level			Row totals
		1	2	3	
Free school meals?	yes	16	64	9	89
	no	23	274	14	311
Column totals		39	338	23	400

Expected, f_e		Key Stage 1 Level			Row totals
		1	2	3	
Free school meals?	yes	8.6775	75.205	5.1175	89
	no	30.3225	262.795	17.8825	311
Column totals		39	338	23	400

2 Which one of the following statements is true?

A For level 1, the difference between observed and expected frequencies is the same for students who do have free school meals and for those who do not. This means that the two contributions to X^2, the test statistic, from these cells will be equal.

B The largest difference between observed and expected frequencies is for level 2 so the largest contributions to X^2, the test statistic, will come from this column.

C The smallest differences between observed and expected frequencies are in the level 3 column. This means that, at the top end of the ability range, there is no association between whether students get free school meals and how well they do in mathematics.

D You need to calculate X^2, the test statistic and the contributions to it from each cell to investigate whether there is any association; it is not enough just to look at the observed and expected frequencies.

3 To test whether there is any association between children's Key Stage 1 mathematics level and their getting free school meals, the hypotheses are as follows.

H_0 : There is no association between mathematics level and getting free school meals

H_1 : There is some association between mathematics level and getting free school meals

Calculate X^2, the test statistic for the data and the contributions to it from individual cells then decide which of the following statements is true.

A The null hypothesis would be rejected, even at the 0.5% level.

B Children who have free school meals do worse in mathematics at Key Stage 1 than children who do not.

C Getting rid of free school meals would result in improvements in mathematics performance.

D There are far too many children on level 2 in the sample.

Exam-Style Question ▷L

A random sample of year 11 students is asked whether they have ever played truant. The results are summarised in the table.

		Have you played truant?			Row totals
		Never	Once or twice	More than twice	
Sex	Male	42	22	28	92
	Female	65	20	18	103
Column totals		107	42	46	195

i) Carry out a suitable test at the 5% significance level to examine whether there is any association between the sex of the students and how often they say they have truanted. State your null and alternative hypotheses carefully. Your working should include a table showing the contributions of each cell to the test statistic.

ii) Discuss briefly how the responses vary between boys and girls, as shown by the contributions to the test statistic.

Bivariate data

Calculating Pearson's product moment correlation coefficient

▶▶ 111
119
133
142

A ABOUT THIS TOPIC

A scatter diagram allows you to judge whether there is correlation in a set of bivariate data. Pearson's product moment correlation coefficient is a way of measuring how strong the correlation is. However, it is more than that, it is a test statistic and this is covered in the next section. Pearson's product moment correlation coefficient is sometimes just called 'the correlation coefficient'.

R REMEMBER

- Scatter diagrams and basic ideas of correlation from GCSE.

K KEY FACTS

- Bivariate data are in pairs so they involve two variables, e.g. age and height of a sample of children. Such data can be plotted on a scatter diagram.

- Correlation means a linear relationship. Pearson's product moment correlation coefficient measures the strength of the linear relationship. It can take values between -1 and $+1$ (inclusive).

- A correlation coefficient of $+1$ means the points all lie in a straight line with positive gradient. A correlation coefficient of -1 means the points all lie in a straight line with negative gradient.

- A correlation coefficient of 0 means there is no correlation, i.e. no linear relationship.

- You should always draw a scatter diagram before calculating a correlation coefficient.

- For a sample of n observations, (x, y)

$$S_{xx} = \sum x^2 - n\bar{x}^2 = \sum x^2 - \frac{(\sum x)^2}{n}$$
$$S_{yy} = \sum y^2 - n\bar{y}^2 = \sum y^2 - \frac{(\sum y)^2}{n}$$
$$S_{xy} = \sum xy - n(\bar{x})(\bar{y}) = \sum xy - \frac{(\sum x)(\sum y)}{n}$$

- Pearson's product moment correlation coefficient (pmcc), $r = \dfrac{S_{xy}}{\sqrt{S_{xx}S_{yy}}}$.

Where does the formula for Pearson's product moment correlation coefficient come from?

The mean of the x and y values, $(\bar{x}, \bar{y})$, is plotted and vertical and horizontal lines drawn through it to divide the scatter diagram into four quadrants.

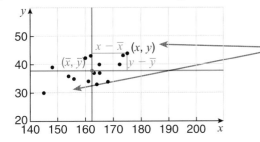

$(x - \bar{x})(y - \bar{y})$ is positive for points in these quadrants; if most points are in these quadrants, that indicates positive correlation. In the other two quadrants, $(x - \bar{x})(y - \bar{y})$ is negative.

$S_{xy} = \sum(x - \bar{x})(y - \bar{y})$ will be positive for positive correlation and negative for negative correlation. The formula $S_{xy} = \sum xy - n(\bar{x})(\bar{y})$ or

$S_{xy} = \sum xy - \dfrac{(\sum x)(\sum y)}{n}$ is easier to use to calculate S_{xy}. It is then divided

by $\sqrt{S_{xx}S_{yy}}$ to give an answer which is between $+1$ and -1.

R RULE

For a sample of n observations, (x, y)

Pearson's product moment correlation coefficient, $r = \dfrac{S_{xy}}{\sqrt{S_{xx}S_{yy}}}$.

EXAMPLE 1

Body mass index (BMI) and resting pulse rate are each used as measures of health. To investigate the relationship between BMI and resting pulse rate, these are measured for a sample of 15 men. The results are shown in the table; summary statistics are given below.

BMI (x)	20.84	30.46	22.1	26.17	27.31	31.91	23.97	27.85	28.6	24.6	30.76	29.59	21.49	24.79	29
Pulse (y)	84	98	62	62	70	68	86	64	48	78	76	68	60	78	84

$\sum x = 399.44$ $\sum y = 1086$ $\sum x^2 = 10\,811.8936$

$\sum y^2 = 80\,892$ $\sum xy = 28\,954.28$ $n = 15$

These are the summary statistics referred to in the question.

Calculate the product moment correlation coefficient for the sample.

SOLUTION

A ADVICE

You have been given summary statistics. You will find it quicker and more accurate to use them than to work with the data from the table. Sometimes you will only be given summary statistics and not the raw data as well.

$S_{xx} = \sum x^2 - \dfrac{(\sum x)^2}{n}$

$S_{xx} = 10\,811.8936 - \dfrac{(399.44)^2}{15}$

$= 175.072\ldots$

Start by working out S_{xx}, S_{yy} and S_{xy}. To work out S_{xx} you can use $S_{xx} = \sum x^2 - n\bar{x}^2$ or $S_{xx} = \sum x^2 - \dfrac{(\sum x)^2}{n}$. The second of these formulae uses the summary statistics directly so you are less likely to go wrong.

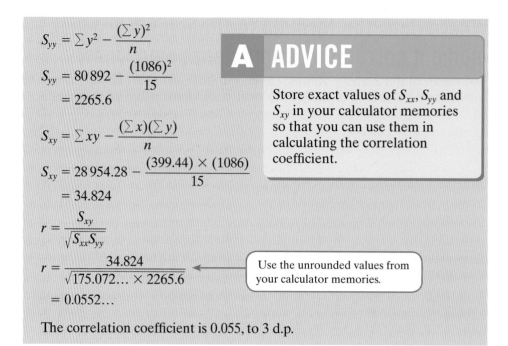

$$S_{yy} = \sum y^2 - \frac{(\sum y)^2}{n}$$

$$S_{yy} = 80\,892 - \frac{(1086)^2}{15}$$

$$= 2265.6$$

$$S_{xy} = \sum xy - \frac{(\sum x)(\sum y)}{n}$$

$$S_{xy} = 28\,954.28 - \frac{(399.44) \times (1086)}{15}$$

$$= 34.824$$

$$r = \frac{S_{xy}}{\sqrt{S_{xx}S_{yy}}}$$

$$r = \frac{34.824}{\sqrt{175.072\ldots \times 2265.6}}$$

$$= 0.0552\ldots$$

The correlation coefficient is 0.055, to 3 d.p.

A ADVICE

Store exact values of S_{xx}, S_{yy} and S_{xy} in your calculator memories so that you can use them in calculating the correlation coefficient.

Use the unrounded values from your calculator memories.

A ADVICE

It is often helpful to draw a scatter diagram when working out a correlation coefficient as it will give you a visual impression of the data. In this case, it would have shown you that there is very little correlation (see below). In some examination questions you will be asked to draw a scatter diagram but don't spend time doing this if you are not going to get any marks for it.

Scatter diagram for Example 1

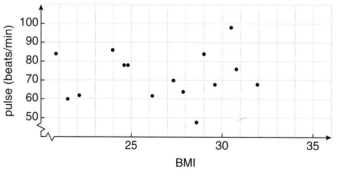
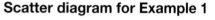

Even if there is strong correlation, it does not mean that change in one of the variables **causes** change in the other variable.

Using the statistical functions on a calculator

Most calculators will let you enter a set of (x, y) values and give you the product moment correlation coefficient at the press of a button. Unfortunately, if you do this in an examination and enter one value incorrectly you will get the wrong correlation coefficient and not have any working written down which you could get marks for. If you are given a table of (x, y) values in an examination question, you can use the calculator statistical functions to get the summary statistics and then use the formula for S_{xx}, S_{yy} and S_{xy}, just as in Example 1.

LINKS

| Statistics | Hypothesis Test using Pearson's Product Moment Correlation Coefficient (S2); Spearman's Rank Correlation Coefficient (S2). |

Test Yourself ▶L

1 The two scatter diagrams show the handspan and height of a sample of teenagers.

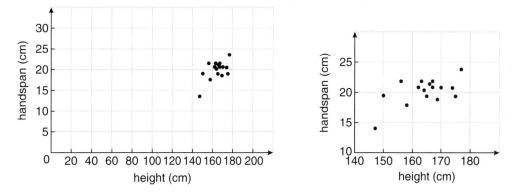

Pearson's product moment correlation coefficient is calculated for the data in each scatter diagram. Which of the following statements is true?

A The correlation coefficient for the first diagram is lower than for the second diagram.

B The correlation coefficients for both diagrams are equal.

C The correlation coefficient for the first diagram is higher than for the second diagram.

D The only way to decide which of A, B or C is true is to work out the correlation coefficient for each diagram.

The following data are for questions 2, 3 and 4.
A researcher is testing whether there is a connection between mathematics ability and ability to solve Sudoku puzzles quickly. A sample of 11 students sit a mathematics test and solve a Sudoku. The results are shown in the table.

Maths test (%)	62	52	78	45	63	89	59	62	73	92	75
Time to solve Sudoku (mins)	26	25	36	32	18	11	17	19	24	15	22

2 Plot the data on a scatter diagram. If the point representing the student who took 36 minutes to solve the Sudoku was removed, what effect would this have on the correlation coefficient?

A The correlation coefficient for the 10 remaining students is nearer to -1 than it was for all 11 students.

B The correlation coefficient for the 10 remaining students is nearer to 0 than it was for all 11 students.

C The correlation coefficient for the 10 remaining students is nearer to 1 than it was for all 11 students.

D The only way to decide which of A, B or C is true is to work out the correlation coefficient for all 11 students and then for the 10 remaining students.

3 Using the data from all 11 students, calculate the value of S_{xy}. (Answers are given to the nearest whole number.)

   A $-15\,229$ B -469 C -466 D 936 E $16\,236$

4 Using the data from all 11 students, calculate the value of Pearson's product moment correlation coefficient. (Answers are given to 4 s.f.)

   A -5494 B -0.5302 C -0.4333 D -0.4328 E -0.0004

Exam-Style Question ◗L

George wants to see how well his computer estimates the time it will take to copy folders. He measures the actual times taken for a sample of folders to copy. The results are shown in the table.

Estimate of time taken (min)	7	6	14	5	10	$\frac{1}{2}$	4	4	1	3	2	3
Actual time taken (min)	8	$7\frac{3}{4}$	$7\frac{1}{4}$	7	$6\frac{3}{4}$	$\frac{1}{4}$	6	$4\frac{1}{4}$	1	4	$2\frac{1}{4}$	2

i) Plot the data on a scatter diagram.

ii) Calculate Pearson's product moment correlation coefficient.

iii) George suspects that removing the two points with the largest estimated times will increase the correlation coefficient. Is he right? Explain your answer without recalculating the correlation coefficient.

Hypothesis tests using Pearson's product moment correlation coefficient

A ABOUT THIS TOPIC

The scatter diagram shows a finite, bivariate population. The red points are a sample from that population. The correlation coefficient can be calculated for the sample. How high does that correlation coefficient have to be to convince us that there is correlation in the whole population? This section shows how to make such decisions.

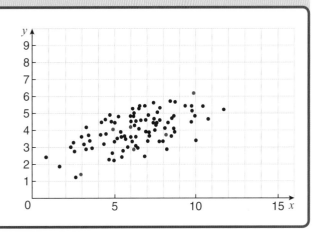

R REMEMBER

- Correlation means a linear relationship. Pearson's product moment correlation coefficient measures the strength of the linear relationship. It can take values between -1 and $+1$ (inclusive).

  For a sample of n observations, (x, y)

$$S_{xx} = \sum x^2 - n\bar{x}^2 = \sum x^2 - \frac{(\sum x)^2}{n}$$

$$S_{yy} = \sum y^2 - n\bar{y}^2 = \sum y^2 - \frac{(\sum y)^2}{n}$$

$$S_{xy} = \sum xy - n(\bar{x})(\bar{y}) = \sum xy - \frac{(\sum x)(\sum y)}{n}$$

- Pearson's product moment correlation coefficient, $r = \dfrac{S_{xy}}{\sqrt{S_{xx}S_{yy}}}$.

K KEY FACTS

- To conduct a hypothesis test using Pearson's product moment correlation coefficient, the data must be from a bivariate Normal population.

- The points in a scatter diagram for a bivariate Normal population lie in an elliptical pattern.

- The null hypothesis, H_0, is that $\rho = 0$ where ρ is the population correlation coefficient. The null hypothesis is that there is no correlation in the population.

- The alternative hypothesis, H_1, will be one of the following:
  - $\rho > 0$ (one-tail test, testing for positive correlation)
  - $\rho < 0$ (one-tail test, testing for negative correlation)
  - $\rho \neq 0$ (two-tail test, testing for some correlation).

- The critical value, from tables, tells you how close to 1 or -1 the sample correlation coefficient has to be for you to reject the null hypothesis that $\rho = 0$.

Bivariate Normal distribution

In an earlier section you saw that for a Normal distribution for one variable, a frequency diagram for the whole population will be a bell-shaped curve, as shown in the diagram.

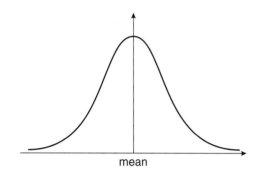

mean

For a bivariate population (two variables, x and y), the frequency density could go on the z axis in three dimensions. For each value of x, y has a Normal distribution and for each value of y, x has a Normal distribution. When a sample from a bivariate Normal population is taken and plotted in a scatter diagram, the points will tend to lie in an elliptical pattern.

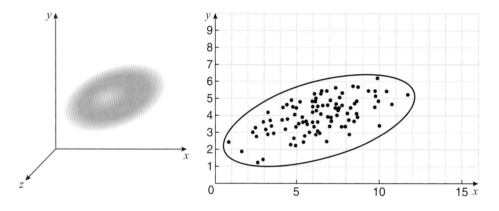

Conducting a hypothesis test

EXAMPLE 1

Verna is making slippers for children. She measures the feet of a random sample of 12 girls. The results are shown in the table.

Foot length	14.4	20.0	13.5	14.7	17.3	16.7
Foot width	5.8	8.0	5.7	5.5	7.2	6.8

Foot length	12.0	18.1	17.8	21.0	19.2	15.4
Foot width	5.2	7.1	6.7	8.5	6.7	6.2

Summary statistics for these data are as follows.

$\sum x = 200.1$ $\qquad$ $\sum y = 79.4$ $\qquad$ $\sum x^2 = 3419.13$
$\sum y^2 = 536.38$ $\qquad$ $\sum xy = 1352.23$ $\qquad$ $n = 12$

i) Calculate the sample product moment correlation coefficient.

ii) Carry out a hypothesis test at the 5% significance level to determine whether there is any correlation between length and width of girls' feet.

SOLUTION

i) $S_{xx} = \sum x^2 - \dfrac{(\sum x)^2}{n}$

$= 3419.13 - \dfrac{200.1^2}{12} = 82.4625$

$S_{yy} = \sum y^2 - \dfrac{(\sum y)^2}{n}$

$= 536.38 - \dfrac{79.4^2}{12} = 11.01666\ldots$

> Do not round the value of S_{yy}. You will need to use it when calculating the sample correlation coefficient, r.

$S_{xy} = \sum xy - \dfrac{(\sum x)(\sum y)}{n}$

$= 1352.23 - \dfrac{200.1 \times 79.4}{12} = 28.235$

$r = \dfrac{S_{xy}}{\sqrt{S_{xx}\,S_{yy}}}$

$= \dfrac{28.235}{\sqrt{82.4625 \times 11.01666\ldots}} = 0.93677\ldots$

> It will save you time, and help you be more accurate, if you have these values in calculator memories.

$r \approx 0.9368$

ii) $H_0 : \rho = 0$

$H_1 : \rho \neq 0$

where ρ is the population correlation coefficient

> Round the correlation coefficient to 4 decimal places as this is what you will get in the tables.

> Start by stating both hypotheses.

A ADVICE

Remember to say what ρ stands for; there will often be a mark for doing this.

⚠ Although the sample correlation coefficient turned out to be positive, the question asked you to test whether there is **any** correlation so the alternative hypothesis is $\rho \neq 0$. It is a 2-tail test.

For $n = 12$, the 5% critical value for a two-tail test is 0.5760.

> Use tables to write down the critical value.

	5%	$2\frac{1}{2}$%	1-Tail Test
	10%	5%	2-Tail Test
n			
12	0.4973	0.5760	

$0.9368 > 0.5760$ so reject the null hypothesis.

> Tables give critical values for the sample correlation coefficient. These are the minimum values needed to provide evidence of correlation in the population. Notice that there is a different row for each value of n.

There is sufficient evidence, at the 5% significance level, of correlation between girls' foot length and width.

A ADVICE

- If the correlation coefficient is negative, you should compare the size of it to the critical value.
- Remember to state your final conclusion in the context you are working in.

Interpreting a correlation coefficient

If there is evidence of correlation it does not mean that change in one of the variables causes change in the other variable. For example, there is a correlation between children's shoe size and reading ability. This is because older children tend to have bigger feet and they also tend to be better at reading; it is not because having bigger feet makes you a better reader.

If there is no correlation, this does not mean there is no relationship between the variables. The relationship might not be a straight line (linear) relationship.

LINKS

Statistics   Hypothesis Tests using Spearman's Rank
Correlation Coefficient (S2).

Test Yourself ▷L

1 A sports coach wants to test whether fast runners are also fast swimmers and vice versa. She asks each of a random sample of athletes to run 200 m and to swim a length of a swimming pool. x is the time in seconds to run 200 m, y is the time in seconds to swim a length. Which of the following should be the hypotheses for her statistical test?

  A $H_0: \rho = 0$ **B** $H_0: \rho = 0$ **C** $H_0: \rho = 0$ **D** $H_0: \rho > 0$ **E** $H_0: \rho > 0$
        $H_1: \rho < 0$ $H_1: \rho \neq 0$ $H_1: \rho > 0$ $H_1: \rho < 0$ $H_1: \rho = 0$

In each of the above, ρ stands for the population correlation coefficient.

2 The sports coach in question 1 finds that the correlation coefficient for her sample is 0.7836. Which of the following statements is true?

  A There is no need to do a hypothesis test. The high positive correlation coefficient shows that people who are fast runners are also fast swimmers.

  B If there were fewer than 6 people in the sample then there is definitely no correlation in the population.

  C If there were 6 or more people in the sample, there is evidence of positive correlation in the population.

  D If you want people to be fast swimmers, you should just train them to run fast then they will be good at both.

  E If there were 9 people in the sample, there is evidence at the 1% level of significance that people who are fast runners are also fast swimmers and vice versa.

The following information is for questions 3 and 4.
A student believes that people who play more computer games tend to have faster reaction times. To test the theory, he asks a random sample of 10 people how long they each spent playing computer games in the last week. He also carries out a reaction time test with each of them. The results are in the table below.

Time on computer games (hours)	2	9	24	0	1	7	10	20	14	7
Reaction time (seconds)	0.465	0.435	0.31	0.485	0.49	0.355	0.21	0.2	0.26	0.285

3 Calculate Pearson's product moment correlation coefficient for these data. (Rounded answers are given to 4 d.p.)

A −5.858   B −0.7252   C −0.7242   D −0.0895   E −0.0280

Make sure you have the right answer to question 3 before going on to question 4.

4 Carry out a hypothesis test, at the 1% significance level, to determine whether people who spend longer on computer games tend to have faster reaction times. Which one of the following statements is true?

A The sample correlation coefficient is negative so there is no evidence that people who spend longer on computer games tend to have faster reaction times.

B This is a one-tail test. The size of the sample correlation coefficient is bigger than the critical value so there is sufficient evidence that people who spend longer on computer games tend to have faster reaction times.

C This is a one-tail test. The sample correlation coefficient is smaller than the critical value so there is insufficient evidence that people who spend longer on computer games tend to have faster reaction times.

D This is a two-tail test. The sample correlation coefficient is bigger than the critical value so there is sufficient evidence that people who spend longer on computer games tend to have faster reaction times.

E This is a two-tail test. The size of the sample correlation coefficient is smaller than the critical value so there is insufficient evidence that people who spend longer on computer games tend to have faster reaction times.

Exam-Style Question ▶▌

Eight history students are chosen at random to sit two examination papers. Their marks are shown in the table.

Paper 1	67	61	58	48	76	53	52	44
Paper 2	73	73	56	55	75	61	61	55

i)   State what distributional assumption is necessary in order to conduct a hypothesis test using Pearson's product moment correlation coefficient on these data.

The examiners say that there should be a positive correlation between the marks on both papers.

ii) Test, at the 5% level, whether the examiners' claim is true. You should state your hypotheses and conclusions clearly.

iii) Another pair of examinations has been tried out on a different random sample of students. The product moment correlation coefficient for the sample was 0.35. A similar hypothesis test to the one in part **ii)** was conducted. This led to an acceptance that there is a positive correlation at the 5% level. How many students could have been in this sample?

Spearman's rank correlation coefficient

A | **ABOUT THIS TOPIC**

Sometimes you suspect that as one variable goes up then so does another but you do not know whether the relationship is a linear one. For example, some scientists think that if the amount of carbon dioxide gas in the atmosphere increases then so will the average temperature at the earth's surface. Spearman's rank correlation coefficient is a way of measuring the strength of relationships that are not necessarily linear.

R | **REMEMBER**

- Correlation means a linear relationship for bivariate data. Pearson's product moment correlation coefficient measures the strength of a linear relationship. It can take values between -1 and $+1$ (inclusive).

K | **KEY FACTS**

- Spearman's rank correlation coefficient measures association between the variables.
- When finding Spearman's rank correlation coefficient, the data for each variable need to be ranked. You can use 1 for either the highest or the lowest value, as long as you do the same for both variables.
- If there are tied ranks, each item gets the average of the ranks they would have had if they had been slightly different.
- Spearman's rank correlation coefficient, r_s, is worked out using the formula $r_s = 1 - \dfrac{6\sum d_i^2}{n(n^2 - 1)}$

  where $d_i = x_i - y_i$ and x_i and y_i denote the ranks of the two variables in data item number i.
- r_s is a test statistic. See section 'Hypothesis tests using Spearman's rank correlation coefficient'.

Introducing Spearman's coefficient of rank correlation

Sometimes you have ranks for the data rather than measurements. This can arise when judges are putting items in order of preference.

EXAMPLE 1

Bob and Marcia are judges for a poster competition. There are seven entries; these are labelled A, B, C, D, E, F and G. Bob and Marcia each put the posters in order, with number 1 being the best. The results are as follows.

	A	B	C	D	E	F	G
Bob (x_i)	3	1	6	5	7	4	2
Marcia (y_i)	5	6	4	3	7	1	2

Calculate the value of Spearman's rank correlation coefficient.

SOLUTION

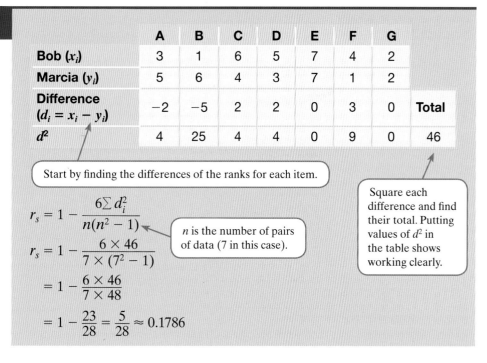

	A	B	C	D	E	F	G	
Bob (x_i)	3	1	6	5	7	4	2	
Marcia (y_i)	5	6	4	3	7	1	2	
Difference ($d_i = x_i - y_i$)	−2	−5	2	2	0	3	0	**Total**
d^2	4	25	4	4	0	9	0	46

Start by finding the differences of the ranks for each item.

Square each difference and find their total. Putting values of d^2 in the table shows working clearly.

$$r_s = 1 - \frac{6\sum d_i^2}{n(n^2 - 1)}$$

n is the number of pairs of data (7 in this case).

$$r_s = 1 - \frac{6 \times 46}{7 \times (7^2 - 1)}$$

$$= 1 - \frac{6 \times 46}{7 \times 48}$$

$$= 1 - \frac{23}{28} = \frac{5}{28} \approx 0.1786$$

A ADVICE

- It is possible to calculate Spearman's rank coefficient of correlation by using the formula for Pearson's coefficient for the ranks but the calculation is easier using the formula
$$r_s = 1 - \frac{6\sum d_i^2}{n(n^2 - 1)}.$$

- 4 decimal places is usually enough for a correlation coefficient.

Sometimes you have data values where one variable tends to increase (or decrease) as the other increases, but the relationship between the variables may not be linear. In that case, Spearman's coefficient of rank correlation will be more appropriate than Pearson's product moment correlation coefficient. Because the relationship might not be linear, Spearman's correlation coefficient is a measure of association (rather than correlation) between the variables.

EXAMPLE 2

A language teacher writes a computer-based module to help her students learn vocabulary. She tests her students before they start using the module. She uses the same test with them some time later when they have used the module. The table below shows the time spent using the module and improvement in test mark.

Time spent using module (min)	7	15	27	35	42	62	83	124	148
Increase in test mark	0	1	0	0	1	14	12	13	15

Calculate Spearman's rank correlation coefficient for these data.

Time spent using module (min)	7	15	27	35	42	62	83	124	148
Time rank (x_i)	1	2	3	4	5	6	7	8	9
Increase in test mark	0	1	0	0	1	14	12	13	15
Test increase rank (y_i)	2	4.5	2	2	4.5	8	6	7	9

Start by ranking the two variables, starting with 1 for the smallest.

A ADVICE

- The three lowest test increases are the same, each is zero. Ranks 1, 2 and 3 would be assigned to these positions so each is given the average of these ranks: $\dfrac{1 + 2 + 3}{3} = 2$.
- The next test increases are 1; there are two of these. They would have ranks 4 and 5 so each gets $\dfrac{4 + 5}{2} = 4.5$.
- For **repeated values**, use the average (mean) of the ranks they would have got if they had been slightly different. The ranks need not be whole numbers in this case.

Time spent using module (min)	7	15	27	35	42	62	83	124	148
Time rank (x_i)	1	2	3	4	5	6	7	8	9
Increase in test mark	0	1	0	0	1	14	12	13	15
Test increase rank (y_i)	2	4.5	2	2	4.5	8	6	7	9
Difference in ranks (d_i)	−1	−2.5	1	2	0.5	−2	1	1	0
d^2	1	6.25	1	4	0.25	4	1	1	0

Total of $d^2 = 18.5$

Remember to find the difference of the ranks.

$$r_s = 1 - \frac{6 \sum d_i^2}{n(n^2 - 1)}$$

$$r_s = 1 - \frac{6 \times 18.5}{9 \times (9^2 - 1)}$$

$n = 9$ because there are 9 data pairs.

$$= 1 - \frac{111}{720}$$

$$= 1 - 0.15416\ldots$$

$$= 0.84583\ldots$$

$$r_s \approx 0.8458$$

What does a value of $r_s = 0.8458$ mean? It is a test statistic, and you will see how to use it in the next section.

Pearson's or Spearman's?

Use Pearson's product moment correlation coefficient in the following situations
- You know the actual data values.

AND
- The relationship between the variables is thought to be linear.

When using Pearson's pmcc in a hypothesis test,
- The variables must come from a bivariate Normal population (see the previous section).
- Both variables must be random (for example, if one of the variables is time, measurements of the other variable should not be taken at regular intervals).

Use Spearman's rank correlation coefficient in the following situations
- You only have ranks not the actual values.

OR
- The relationship between the variables may not be linear.

> **A** | **ADVICE**
>
> Exam questions will usually tell you which correlation coefficient to use but you may be asked why one is appropriate but not the other.

LINKS

Statistics   Hypothesis Tests using Spearman's Rank Correlation Coefficient (S2).

Test Yourself ▶L

1 Sammy and Fran are trying to decide which hotel to book for a holiday. There are 5 possible hotels and each of them puts the hotels in order of preference.

	Hotel Splendid	Sea View Hotel	Comfort Lodge	Bella Vista Hotel	Grand Hotel
Sammy	1	3	4	2	5
Fran	4	2	3	1	5

Calculate Spearman's coefficient of rank correlation.

A −0.5917 (4 d.p.)   B 0.4   C 0.6   D 0.7   E 1

These data are for questions 2 and 3.
A sample of 8 primary school students take a reading test and a writing test. Their test levels are shown in the table below.

Reading level	2	3	3	4	4	4	5	5
Writing level	2	2	3	3	4	3	4	5

2 Which are the correct ranks for the data above?

A

Reading level	2	3	3	4	4	4	5	5
Reading rank	1	2	3	4	5	6	7	8
Writing level	2	2	3	3	4	3	4	5
Writing rank	1	2	3	4	6	5	7	8

B

Reading level	2	3	3	4	4	4	5	5
Reading rank	1	2	2	3	3	3	4	4
Writing level	2	2	3	3	4	3	4	5
Writing rank	1	1	2	2	3	2	3	4

C

Reading level	2	3	3	4	4	4	5	5
Reading rank	1	2.5	2.5	4	4	4	5.5	5.5
Writing level	2	2	3	3	4	3	4	5
Writing rank	1.5	1.5	3	3	4.5	3	4.5	5

D

Reading level	2	3	3	4	4	4	5	5
Reading rank	1	2.5	2.5	5	5	5	7.5	7.5
Writing level	2	2	3	3	4	3	4	5
Writing rank	1.5	1.5	4	4	6.5	4	6.5	8

Make sure you have the right answer to question 2 before doing question 3.

3 What is Spearman's coefficient of rank correlation for the data in question 2? (Answers are given to 4 d.p.)

A -0.1052 B 0.1071   C 0.8929   D 0.9524   E 0.9821

4 Four statements about correlation coefficients are given below. Three of them are false and one is true. Which one is true?

A If you know the actual values of the data (not just ranks) it is always better to use Pearson's product moment correlation coefficient rather than Spearman's rank correlation coefficient.

B If you work out Pearson's product moment correlation coefficient and Spearman's rank correlation coefficient for a set of data, they will each give exactly the same answer.

C Ranking data loses information so Pearson's product moment correlation coefficient uses more of the information than Spearman's rank correlation coefficient.

D If Spearman's rank correlation coefficient is close to 1 or -1, it would definitely be easy to draw a straight line of best fit on the scatter diagram.

Exam-Style Question ▶L

A local show includes a fruit cake competition. Five cakes are entered and they are labelled A, B, C, D and E. Two judges, Ben and Bob, taste samples of all five cakes with results as shown:

Position	1st	2nd	3rd	4th	5th
Ben	B	D	C	E	A
Bob	A	D	B	E	C

i) Calculate Spearman's rank correlation coefficient for Ben and Bob's rankings.

Cake A is disqualified from the competition because it has been made by Bob's sister.

ii) Assuming that neither Ben or Bob change their minds about the rank order of the other 4 cakes, copy and complete the table.

Position	1st	2nd	3rd	4th
Ben				
Bob				

iii) Calculate Spearman's rank correlation coefficient for Ben and Bob's rankings of the 4 remaining cakes.

iv) Comment on the effect of removing cake A on Spearman's rank correlation coefficient.

Hypothesis tests using Spearman's rank correlation coefficient

In a sample of bivariate data, you have two variables for each item. You often want to know if they change together in some way. A hypothesis test using Spearman's rank correlation coefficient can be used in circumstances where Pearson's product moment correlation coefficient cannot be used; for example, when the relationship is not linear.

R REMEMBER

- Spearman's rank correlation coefficient measures association between the variables.
- When finding Spearman's rank correlation coefficient, the data for each variable need to be ranked. You can use 1 for either the highest or the lowest value, as long as you do the same for both variables.
- If there are tied ranks, each item gets the average of the ranks they would have had if they had been slightly different.
- Spearman's rank correlation coefficient, r_s, is worked out using the formula

$$r_s = 1 - \frac{6\sum d_i^2}{n(n^2 - 1)} \text{ where } d_i = x_i - y_i,$$

and x_i and y_i denote ranks of data.

K KEY FACTS

- The null hypothesis, H_0, is that there is no association between the variables. The null hypothesis should be given in words.

- The alternative hypothesis, H_1, will be one of the following:
  - There is positive association between the variables (one-tail test).
  - There is negative association between the variables (one-tail test).
  - There is some association between the variables (two-tail test).

- The critical value, from tables, tells you how high Spearman's rank correlation coefficient has to be for the sample for you to reject the null hypothesis (that there is no association between the variables).

How high does Spearman's rank correlation coefficient need to be?

In Example 2 of the previous section, you worked out Spearman's rank correlation coefficient for a sample of students who used a computer-based module to help them learn vocabulary. Is the rank correlation coefficient high enough to indicate that students who use the computer module more tend to improve their vocabulary more?

EXAMPLE 1

A language teacher writes a computer-based module to help her students learn vocabulary. She tests her students before they start using the module. She uses the same test with them some time later when they have used the module. The table below shows the time spent using the module and improvement in test mark.

Time spent using module (min)	7	15	27	35	42	62	83	124	148
Increase in test mark	0	1	0	0	1	14	12	13	15

In Example 2 of the previous section, you worked out Spearman's rank correlation coefficient to be 0.8458. Carry out a hypothesis test at the 5% level to determine whether there is positive association between time spent using the module and increase in test mark.

SOLUTION

The hypotheses for the test are :

H_0: There is no association between time spent using the computer module and increase in test mark for language students.

H_1: There is positive association between time spent using the computer module and increase in test mark.

A ADVICE

Both hypotheses should be given in words; the null hypothesis is always that there is no association between the variables but you should refer to the actual variables in the situation that you are performing the hypothesis test for. Notice that the test is for the population of language students in general but it uses the data from the sample of 9 students.

⚠ You will notice that both Spearman's test and the χ^2 test for contingency tables (see section 'The χ^2 test for independence in a contingency table') have the same null hypothesis of 'no association'. For a test using Spearman's rank correlation coefficient, the alternative hypothesis can be one-tailed or two-tailed whereas it is always that there is some association (two-tailed) for the χ^2 test. The two tests are used in quite different circumstances so be careful to use the right one.

Spearman's rank correlation coefficient is 0.8458, $n = 9$.

This is a one-tail test as you are looking for evidence of positive association.

> There were 9 data pairs in the sample.

The critical value is 0.6000.

	5%	$2\frac{1}{2}$%	1-Tail Test
	10%	5%	2-Tail Test
n			
1	–	–	
9	0.6000	0.7000	

0.8458 > 0.6000 so there is sufficient evidence of positive association at the 5% level.

There is evidence of positive association between time spent using the module and improvement in test mark.

A ADVICE

You should always state the final conclusion in words, relating it to the original situation. There is often a mark in the exam for doing this. In this case, the wording used in the example would be one way to do this.

What does the hypothesis test result mean?

Students who spend longer using the computer module tend to improve more in the test. There is a temptation to think that making students use the module for longer will result in improved test marks. However, this need not be the case. The module could be helping students to improve or it might be that students who would do well anyway tend to be the ones who use the computer module more.

Even if there is association between the variables, Spearman's rank correlation coefficient cannot tell whether change in one variable is causing change in the other variable.

Which hypothesis test?

Remember that to use the hypothesis test using Pearson's product moment correlation coefficient, the data need to be from a bivariate Normal population (see section 'Hypothesis tests using Pearson's product moment correlation coefficient'). If they are, then it is better to use Pearson's product moment correlation coefficient as it uses actual values rather than ranks so no information is lost.

A ADVICE

If you get an exam question where either test could be used and you are asked why it is better to use Pearson's product moment correlation coefficient, remember to say that it uses all the information as well as explaining that it uses actual values rather than ranks.

EXAMPLE 2   Draw a scatter diagram for the data in Example 1. The language teacher decides to use a hypothesis test using Pearson's product moment correlation coefficient as it will use more information and so be more accurate. Is she right to use Pearson's product moment correlation coefficient?

SOLUTION

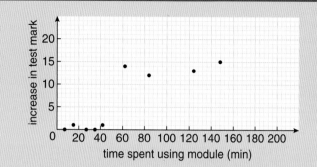

To use Pearson's product moment correlation coefficient, the data need to be from a bivariate Normal population. The scatter diagram for a sample from such a population will have the points lying in an approximate ellipse. These points do not look as if they lie in an approximate ellipse and the sample is small so you should be wary of drawing conclusions from using Pearson's product moment correlation coefficient.

LINKS

Statistics   Kendall's Rank Correlation Coefficient (beyond A level).

Test Yourself ▷L

This information is for questions 1 to 4.
A student is doing a project on the factors which affect used car price. He finds the prices of a random sample of used cars, all made in the same year. The following table shows the engine sizes and prices of the cars.

Engine size (litres)	2.0	2.0	1.25	1.8	1.8	1.0	3.0	1.8	3.3	1.6
Price (£)	7 000	2 495	1 599	1 995	2 995	999	3 495	2 195	7 950	995

The student will do a hypothesis test using Spearman's rank correlation coefficient to see if there is evidence of association between engine size and price.

1 Which are suitable null and alternative hypotheses to use for such a test?

A $\left. \begin{array}{l} H_0 : \rho = 0 \\ H_1 : \rho \neq 0 \end{array} \right\}$ where ρ is the population correlation coefficient.

B $\left. \begin{array}{l} H_0 : \rho = 0 \\ H_1 : \rho > 0 \end{array} \right\}$ where ρ is the population correlation coefficient.

C H_0 : There is no association between the variables.
H_1 : There is some association between the variables.

D H_0 : There is no association between engine size and price.
H_1 : There is some association between engine size and price.

E H_0 : There is no correlation between engine size and price.
H_1 : There is some correlation between engine size and price.

2 What is the value of Spearman's rank correlation coefficient?
(Rounded answers are given to 4 d.p.)

A −0.0996   B 0.7303   C 0.8636   D 0.9   E 0.9833

3 What is the critical region for the hypothesis test at the 5% level of significance?

A $r_s = 0.5636$ B $r_s > 0.5636$ C $r_s = 0.6319$

D $r_s = 0.6485$ E $|r_s| > 0.6485$

Make sure you have the right answers to questions 2 and 3 before doing question 4.

4 Which of the following is the best way of stating the final conclusion to the hypothesis test at the 5% level of significance?

A Accept the null hypothesis.

B Reject the null hypothesis.

C There is sufficient evidence of association between the variables.

D There is sufficient evidence that there is association between engine size and price.

E There is sufficient evidence that large engine size tends to go with high price.

Exam-Style Question ◗L

The following table shows the mean maximum temperature in April and the total April rainfall. The data are for a random sample of 12 years.

Temp (°C)	9.3	14.5	11.4	11.6	13.3	13.5	13.9	18.1	15.2	12.0	15.4	14.0
Rain (mm)	23.8	10.4	28.1	97.7	19.6	43.1	70.5	1.6	35.9	55.7	19.2	9.6

Data from Royston (Iceni) weather station.

i) Calculate Spearman's rank correlation coefficient for the data.

ii) The highest rainfall is 97.7 mm. A geography student thinks this might be an error and perhaps this figure should be 77.7 mm. Without recalculating the correlation coefficient, explain what effect it would have on Spearman's rank correlation coefficient if the figure was 77.7.

iii) The geography student thinks that warmer Aprils tend to have less rain. Write down suitable hypotheses for a test of this using Spearman's rank correlation coefficient.

iv) Conduct the test at the 5% level of significance, stating your conclusions clearly.

The least squares regression line

A · ABOUT THIS TOPIC

If a scatter diagram shows an approximate linear relationship between two variables, you may well want to know the equation of the straight line which best describes the relationship. This section gives a way of calculating the equation of the straight line.

R · REMEMBER

- $S_{xx} = \sum(x_i - \bar{x})^2 = \sum x_i^2 - \dfrac{(\sum x_i)^2}{n}$
  $= \sum x_i^2 - n\bar{x}^2.$
- $S_{xy} = \sum(x_i - \bar{x})(y_i - \bar{y})$
  $= \sum x_i y_i - \dfrac{(\sum x_i)(\sum y_i)}{n}$
  $= \sum x_i y_i - n(\bar{x})(\bar{y}).$
- The equation of a straight line graph from C1.

K · KEY FACTS

- The **independent** variable goes on the x axis of a scatter diagram and the **dependent** variable goes on the y axis.

- **Residuals** are vertical distances of data points from the regression line. Points above the line have a positive residual. Points below the line have a negative residual.

- The least squares regression line goes through the mean point $(\bar{x}, \bar{y})$.

- The equation of the least squares regression line of y on x is

$$y - \bar{y} = b(x - \bar{x}) \text{ where } b = \frac{S_{xy}}{S_{xx}}.$$

Residuals

The scatter diagram below shows the weight of strawberries picked by a fruit picker. Readings of the weight of fruit picked were taken every 2 minutes.

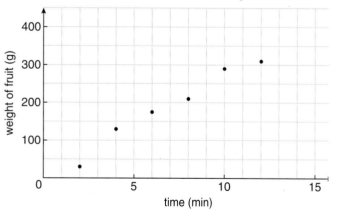

It looks as though a linear relationship would describe the data quite well.

A · ADVICE

The independent variable goes on the x axis. In this case, the experimenter is interested in how weight of fruit picked depends on time, so time is the *independent variable* and weight of fruit picked is the *dependent variable*.

If a straight line is drawn to show the relationship, it cannot go through all the points because the correlation is not perfect.

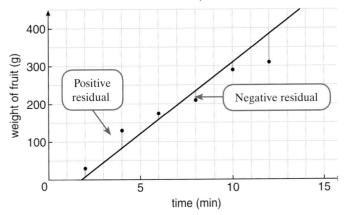

A ADVICE

The distance of a point from the line showing the relationship is called the **residual**. It is measured in a vertical direction. It shows how much the measured value of the dependent variable differs from the value predicted by the straight line.

What is the least squares regression line?

If a line of best fit is drawn in by looking to see where it might go then different people might draw slightly different lines. For a line which shows the relationship well, the sum of the residuals should be zero. The least squares regression line is the line which minimises the sum of squares of the residuals.

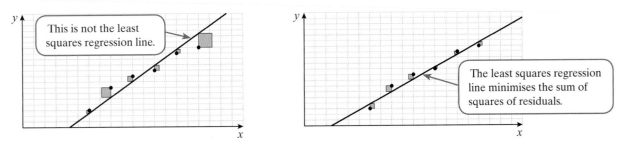

The equation of the least squares regression line of y on x is $y - \bar{y} = b(x - \bar{x})$

where $b = \dfrac{S_{xy}}{S_{xx}}$ and $S_{xx} = \sum x_i^2 - \dfrac{(\sum x_i)^2}{n} = \sum x_i^2 - n\bar{x}^2$,

$S_{xy} = \sum x_i y_i - \dfrac{(\sum x_i)(\sum y_i)}{n} = \sum x_i y_i - n(\bar{x})(\bar{y})$

EXAMPLE 1

The following are the summary statistics for the data from the graph about the fruit picker. x is the time in minutes and y is the weight of fruit picked in grams.

$\sum x = 42$ $\sum x^2 = 364$ $n = 6$

$\sum y = 1137.41$ $\sum y^2 = 269\,169$ $\sum xy = 9865.3$

Find the equation of the least squares regression line.

A ADVICE

Exam questions will often give the summary statistics, as in Example 1, so you must be able to use the formulae to find the regression line. Many scientific calculators will allow you to enter the raw data pairs to get the equation of the line but you cannot show any working if you do this. Using the summary statistics does allow you to show working; this means that you can get some marks even if you go wrong. You can get the summary statistics from a scientific calculator if only the raw data are given in the question.

SOLUTION

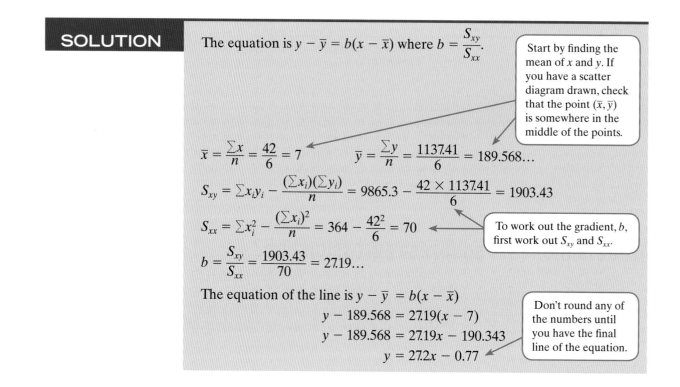

The equation is $y - \bar{y} = b(x - \bar{x})$ where $b = \dfrac{S_{xy}}{S_{xx}}$.

> Start by finding the mean of x and y. If you have a scatter diagram drawn, check that the point $(\bar{x}, \bar{y})$ is somewhere in the middle of the points.

$$\bar{x} = \frac{\sum x}{n} = \frac{42}{6} = 7 \qquad \bar{y} = \frac{\sum y}{n} = \frac{1137.41}{6} = 189.568\ldots$$

$$S_{xy} = \sum x_i y_i - \frac{(\sum x_i)(\sum y_i)}{n} = 9865.3 - \frac{42 \times 1137.41}{6} = 1903.43$$

$$S_{xx} = \sum x_i^2 - \frac{(\sum x_i)^2}{n} = 364 - \frac{42^2}{6} = 70$$

> To work out the gradient, b, first work out S_{xy} and S_{xx}.

$$b = \frac{S_{xy}}{S_{xx}} = \frac{1903.43}{70} = 27.19\ldots$$

The equation of the line is $y - \bar{y} = b(x - \bar{x})$
$$y - 189.568 = 27.19(x - 7)$$
$$y - 189.568 = 27.19x - 190.343$$
$$y = 27.2x - 0.77$$

> Don't round any of the numbers until you have the final line of the equation.

A ADVICE

Give your final answer in the form $y = mx + c$ and have a look at the scatter diagram to check that the gradient and y intercept are reasonable. In this case, the gradient should be positive and the y intercept should be small and negative.

Interpolation and extrapolation

Interpolation is estimating for a data point within the range of points you already have. For Example 1, using the regression line to estimate the amount of fruit picked in 5 minutes would be interpolation.

Extrapolation is using the regression line beyond the range of points you already have. For Example 1, using the regression line to estimate the amount of fruit picked in 15 minutes or in 30 minutes would each be examples of extrapolation.

> ⚠ Interpolation is reasonably reliable but extrapolation may not be. You do not know that the straight-line relationship will continue.

EXAMPLE 2

Use the equation of the regression line from Example 1 to estimate the weight of fruit the picker would pick in

i) 15 minutes

ii) 30 minutes.

Comment on the reliability of your answers.

SOLUTION

$y = 27.2x - 0.77$

i) $x = 15 \Rightarrow y = 27.2 \times 15 - 0.77 = 407.23$

ii) $x = 30 \Rightarrow y = 27.2 \times 30 - 0.77 = 815.23$

The answer for 15 minutes is likely to be fairly reliable because 15 is near to the data in the scatter diagram. The answer for 30 minutes will be less reliable as it is further from the data; it assumes the straight line relationship will continue but the picker may get tired and slow down with time.

Test Yourself ▶L

The following data are for questions 1 to 4.
Fred exercises for 30 minutes then observes his pulse rate in beats per minute after stopping the exercise. The data are shown in the table.

Time after exercise (min) x	$\frac{1}{2}$	1	$1\frac{1}{2}$	2	$2\frac{1}{2}$
Pulse rate y	133	127	98	67	68

1 Which of the following is the value of S_{xy} for the data above?

   A −610.6   B −95   C 2.2   D 496.6   E 644.5

Make sure you have the right answer for question 1 before going on to question 2.

2 Calculate the equation of the regression line of y on x.

   A $y - 98.6 = -38x - 1.5$ B $y = -38x + 41.6$ C $y = -38x + 155.6$

   D $y = 38x + 41.6$ E $y = 155.6x - 38$

Make sure you have the right answer for question 2 before going on to question 3.

3 Calculate the value of the residual for $x = 1$.

   A −9.4   B 0   C 9.4   D 88.36   E 117.6

4 Three of the following statements are false and one is true. Find the one that is true.

   A It would be reasonable to use the equation of the regression line to find the pulse rate 4 minutes after exercise as this is not far from the data in the table.

   B The equation of the regression line which you have found will apply to the pulse rate of all men who exercise for 30 minutes then stop.

   C Time after exercise is the dependent variable and pulse rate is the independent variable.

   D 79.6 is a prediction of Fred's pulse rate 2 minutes after he stops exercise.

5 The scatter diagram has the least squares regression line of y on x drawn on it. Which of the following could be the equation of the regression line?

A $y = -1.1x - 3.3$

B $y = -1.1x + 3.3$

C $y = 1.1x - 3.3$

D $y = 1.1x + 3.3$

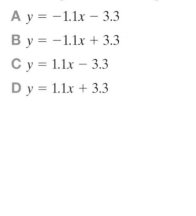

Exam-Style Question ▷L

An experiment to see how much a spring stretches when different weights are hung from it results in the following data:

Mass (g)	50	100	150	200	250	300
Extension (cm)	3	7	9	10	14	15

i) Plot the points on a scatter diagram.

ii) Find the equation of the least squares regression line of y on x, where x is the mass in grams and y is the extension in centimetres. You may use the following summary statistics.

$n = 6$ $\quad\quad\quad\sum x = 1050$ $\quad\quad\quad\sum y = 58$

$\sum x^2 = 227\,500$ $\quad\quad\sum y^2 = 660$ $\quad\quad\sum xy = 12\,200$

iii) Use the equation to predict the extension for a mass of 80 grams.

iv) Comment on whether it would be reliable to use the equation to predict the extension for a mass of 500 grams.

v) Calculate the value of the residual for $x = 100$ and explain how its sign is related to the scatter diagram.

Index

area under the curve, in Normal distribution 26, 28, 31

bell-shaped curve, Normal distribution 26, 36, 80
binomial distribution
    approximating 43, 48
    Poisson approximation 21–5
binomial random variable
    expectation 41, 42
    variance 41
bivariate data 74–99
bivariate distribution, discrete 28
bivariate Normal distribution 80

calculator
    statistical functions 76
    see also graphical calculator
chi-squared (χ^2) test, for independence in a contingency table 65–8, 90, 100
    test statistic 69–73
conditional probability 19
contingency tables 65–8, 69–73, 90, 100
continuity correction 36, 38, 39
correlation coefficient 74–7, 79, 89–93
    interpreting 82
    see also Pearson's product moment correlation; Spearman's rank correlation coefficient
critical region 57
cumulative probability tables 5–7

data
    ranking 84–7
    raw 75, 96
de Moivre, Abraham 41
dependent variable 94
discrete random variables 1, 6, 11
    approximating 36, 38, 39
discrete situations, modelling 38–41

e (exponential) 2, 3
errors, in measurements 36
expectation
    binomial random variable 41, 42
    definition 1
    Poisson distribution 46
expected frequency 13, 69–73
extrapolation 96

factorial 1
frequencies, observed and expected 69–73

graphical calculator
    binomial probabilities 42
    cumulative Poisson probabilities 8–9
    Normal distribution 27

hypothesis
    alternative 55, 60
    null 55–6, 60

hypothesis testing
    one-tail test 55–9
    two-tail test 60–4
    using Pearson's product moment correlation coefficient 74–7
    using Spearman's rank correlation coefficient 84–7
    which test to use 67, 91

independence, testing 65–8, 90, 100
independent events, modelling 1, 2, 6
inequalities, symbols 8
interpolation 96
inverse Normal probability tables 31–2

least squares regression line 94–7
linear relationship 84, 94
line of best fit 95

mean
    finding from probability 33–4
    Normal distribution 26, 29, 36
    one-tail hypothesis test 55–9
    Poisson distribution 3–4, 12–13, 46
    population 52, 56
    sample 50–1, 53, 60
    two-tail hypothesis test 60–4
modelling
    discrete situations 38–41
    independent events 1, 2, 6
    using the Normal distribution 36–7
    using a Poisson distribution 11–15

non-linear relationship 84, 89
Normal approximation
    to the binomial distribution 41–5
    to the Poisson distribution 43–4, 46–9
Normal distribution
    for analysis of errors 36
    area under the curve 26, 28, 31
    bell-shaped curve 26, 36, 80
    bivariate 80
    continuous 28, 36
    mean, standard deviation and variance 26, 29, 36
    one-tail hypothesis test for the mean 55–9
    probability tables 26–32
    random sample 50
    standardising 27, 29, 42
    symmetry 28–9, 36
    two-tail hypothesis test for the mean 60–4

one-tail hypothesis test for the mean 55–9

Pearson's product moment correlation 74–7, 87
Poisson approximation, to the binomial distribution 21–5
Poisson distribution 1–25
    discrete 28
    expectation and variance 46

with large mean 46
    mean and variance 3–4, 12–13
    normal approximation 46–8
    skew 46
    sum of two or more 16–19
Poisson probability formula 2–3
Poisson probability tables 5–10
population
    mean 52, 56
    parameters, likely values 52
    variance 50
probability
    conditional 19
    rules 1
probability tables
    cumulative 5–7
    inverse Normal 31–2
    Normal distribution 26–32
    Poisson 5–10
product moment correlation and regression *see* Pearson's product moment correlation
p-value 58

random sample *see* sample
random variables
    approximating 36, 38, 39
    binomial 41, 42
    discrete 1, 6, 11
ranking of data 84–7
regression 94–7
residuals 94–5

sample
    mean 50–1, 53, 60
    size 51, 52
sampling distribution 50–1
scatter diagrams 74, 76, 79, 94
Spearman's rank correlation coefficient 84–7, 90
standard deviation
    definition 1
    finding from probability 33–4
    Normal distribution 26, 29, 36
    not known 62
straight line, equation of 95, 96

tables *see* contingency tables; probability tables
test statistic 55, 56, 57, 60, 74, 100
    in chi-squared test 69–73
two-tail hypothesis test for the mean 60–4

variance
    binomial random variable 41
    definition 1
    Normal distribution 26, 29, 36
    Poisson distribution 3–4, 12–13, 46
    population 50
    sample mean 51, 53

words, translating to symbols 8

Formulae and results

Statistics 2 results that are not given in the examination booklet

You are also expected to recall or derive Statistics 1 results that are not given in the examination booklet.

The χ^2 test on a contingency table

The test statistic is $X^2 = \sum \dfrac{(f_o - f_e)^2}{f_e}$.

For a contingency table with r rows and c columns there are $(r - 1)(c - 1)$ degrees of freedom.

Product moment correlation and regression

The formulae are given in the examination booklet but you are advised to work with the forms using sums of squares and sums of products, as given below.

Correlation coefficient: $r = \dfrac{S_{xy}}{\sqrt{S_{xx}S_{yy}}}$

Least squares regression line: $y - \bar{y} = b(x - \bar{x})$ where $b = \dfrac{S_{xy}}{S_{xx}}$